liverpool biennial

Contents

liverpool biennial

Editors
Lewis Biggs, Paul Domela,
Sacha Waldron, Andrew Kirk

Cover image
Wolves image by Carlos Amorales,
commissioned by Liverpool Biennial
as part of the *Touched* creative
campaign.

Graphic design
Alan Ward
@ axisgraphicdesign.co.uk

Printing
Andrew Kilburn Print Services Ltd,
Leeds

Published by
Liverpool Biennial of
Contemporary Art Ltd

ISBN 978-0-9536761-8-7

Touched – The Book
Published March 2011

Touched – The Book is more than
a catalogue. Both reader and
catalogue, it sets the exhibition
within a wider theoretical field.

With contributions by Franco
'Bifo' Berardi, Lewis Biggs, Tony
Chakar, Steven Connor, Simon
Critchley, Paul Domela, Coco Fusco,
Lorenzo Fusi, David Harvey, Lynn
Hershman and Alison Rowley,
Alfonso Lingis, Chantal Mouffe, Nina
Power, Abdoumaliq Simone, WHW,
Ziauddin Sardar and others.

With photographic documentation
of the entire exhibition by Thierry Bal
and Mishka Henner & Liz Lock.

Advance copies can be ordered at
www.biennial.com or by completing
an order form available from the
Visitor Centre and *Touched* venues.

Preface

As I write this, Liverpool Biennial 2010 is beginning to make its lupine presence felt across the city and we are preparing for the influx of artists, curators, press and visitors from around the corner and around the world. It is an exciting moment for all of us, particularly the team of international curators, led this year by Lorenzo Fusi, who have commissioned the artists whose work will be seen across the city.

Liverpool residents have always been enthusiastic supporters of what has become the UK's Biennial, and we expect that, as in 2008, visitor numbers will be swelled by those coming from all over the country and abroad. Its reputation as one of the world's foremost biennials in terms of visitors is matched this year by the largest number of artists and works that Liverpool Biennial has ever exhibited.

We will all be touched by the work spread throughout the city, but this year the Biennial has a focus on the Lime Street / Renshaw Street corridor, which stands as a perfect place to demonstrate our belief that great art, commissioned from the best international artists, creates local growth.

Touched is indeed the theme for this year's *International* exhibition – communicating with and involving people in all sorts of ways, enabling personal exploration of sometimes challenging work. The Board

is grateful to the staff who have worked so hard for the last eighteen months to realise this and to the artists who are making this festival another one to remember. We also recognise that the Biennial is a collaboration, delivered by the energy, ideas and enthusiasm of a great many partner organisations and artists who produce such a plethora of work across so many venues.

The Board is grateful too to all the funders without whom the festival would not be possible. Our principal funders – Arts Council England, Liverpool City Council, the European Regional Development Fund (ERDF), and the Northwest Regional Development Agency (NWDA) together with Liverpool Vision – share a commitment to everything the Biennial achieves. But we are also grateful to our many project supporters and sponsors, who believe, like us, that though investment might be relatively small, the rewards are huge.

Explore, entertain and inform yourselves, but most of all, enjoy it!

Paula Ridley, Chairman
Liverpool Biennial

Foreword

Over the past decade there have been few better barometers of Liverpool's cultural trajectory than the rise of Liverpool Biennial. Those who know and love Liverpool understand that this is a city blessed with remarkable cultural assets and the best visual arts provision of any UK city outside London. But when Liverpool Biennial began in 1999, the city's ability to make and present great art in a global context was not recognised well enough beyond its boundaries.

Liverpool now enjoys an international reputation for culture, which has nourished continued investment in the city and an increase in visitor numbers. In many ways, Liverpool Biennial instituted the principles on which Liverpool's accolade as European Capital of Culture 2008 was built: the intersection of the international and the local, ambitious commissioning, and a collaborative model for engaging art, people and place.

The compelling contribution that Liverpool Biennial continues to make to the city, and to the country, is great art. The Biennial brings the very best art to the public: art that is challenging, uncompromising and free-thinking, just like the people of Liverpool. It is a unique platform from which to showcase the city – exhibiting in venues ranging from national galleries to on-street locations. The international artists at the heart of the festival, rubbing shoulders with myriad local artists and the exhibitions they produce, creates a critical mass of art we can be proud of, and which is not seen in any other UK regional city.

The festival attracts huge public and media interest, generates international profile and stimulates debate on the role of art and the role of cities. The economic impact is significant – visitors spent £26 million in 2008 – and it generates jobs and enhances skills in the city and the region, but the Biennial's artistic identity and vital role in the UK's cultural calendar is also integral to the creative reputation of Liverpool.

The Biennial's success comes down to its partnerships. It is an organisation that builds on the strengths of its cultural partners, and the commitment of its stakeholders. Together, they create an impact greater than the sum of their parts. Liverpool Biennial makes a remarkable contribution to the cultural life of the UK and to the visitors from around the world who value the very best in culture.

Few cities can boast such an extraordinary event and we join together to celebrate the contributions that Liverpool Biennial makes to Liverpool and to enriching all our cultural lives.

Dame Liz Forgan, Chair,
Arts Council England

Robert Hough, Chair,
Northwest Regional Development Agency

Cllr Joe Anderson, Leader,
Liverpool City Council

Filip Gilissen
The Winner Takes It All, 2008
Installation still, sensor and counting unit set at 1000 pax.
Dimensions varying over time, 3 Arena CO_2 Shooter,
100,000 slow fall golden glitters, 80 sec, sun-strips, liquid air
Paving event for Liverpool Biennial 2010, 14 May 2010

Touched Preface

The International exhibition for Liverpool Biennial this year presents the work of over 60 artists; around half were commissioned to make new work. The exhibition takes place in five art galleries – A Foundation, the Bluecoat, FACT (Foundation for Art and Creative Technology), Open Eye Gallery, Tate Liverpool – and several non-gallery sites as well. The most prominent of these is in Renshaw Street, where there are three further groupings of artworks within the exhibition: paintings not previously exhibited in the UK under the title *The Human Stain* (page 42); installations and actions that re-animate a disused shop with the aim of *Re:Thinking Trade* (page 26); and the final act of Tania Bruguera's legendary *Cátedra Arte de Conducta* from Havana, with continuing actions over the ten weeks by twenty Cuban artists reinventing Allan Kaprow's *Happenings* (page 22).

The show was developed in dialogue, the curator from each gallery elaborating her or his own particular interest in the overall theme *Touched*; the artists share the practice of contemporary art as a globalised activity, but the value of their work comes from their ability to communicate the specifics of their cultural experience and viewpoint. The curatorial team started with the recognition that the practice of some artists (and it's not such a large number) speaks directly to a wide variety of individuals from different cultures, without mediation, without the intercession of saleroom or celebrity.

What defines art that has this ability to communicate directly, this width of cross-cultural appeal? Emotional experience is common to all humanity. Art that evokes emotion in one individual, despite all the cultural specifics that determine that person's reactions, will reach out to many other individuals with varied cultural backgrounds.

Touched presents art with emotional impact. Art that not only can gain our attention but that can move us, motivate us, allow us to find a way to change ourselves. Art without emotional force is without intellectual power.

Brian McMaster, in his 2008 report *Excellence in the Arts,* suggests that 'excellence in culture occurs when an experience affects and changes an individual. An excellent cultural experience goes to the root of living.'

While we may believe strongly in making art as accessible as possible, the experience of the best art does not come entirely 'free'. In some sense it's an attack on our individual sovereignty, by requiring us to find commonality with others. So the best art is not to everyone's taste. Who can afford the time, attention, energy to be touched? To be touched, it is necessary to be bold, to be vulnerable.

I want to thank the artists, the curatorial team and all the staff of Liverpool Biennial for the good times, and less good times, we shared in realising this exhibition and the 2010 festival.

Lewis Biggs, Artistic Director,
Liverpool Biennial

Touched

The English language is playful: touched in the head, touched in the heart, touched by hand are common expressions, common experiences.

To say that someone is touched in the head is to suggest their closeness to an edge, maybe of madness or of genius, territories lying just beyond the borders of our common humanity. Some artists adopt this state knowingly and with the intention of returning to humanity. In this show Tehching Hsieh and Sachiko Abe have adopted an 'extreme' position in relation to durational time, while Antti Laitinen's devotion to failure might seem extreme also.

To be touched in the heart or the gut is to feel the pull of tragedy in another person's situation; maybe as a result to be moved by horror turning to anger and the desire to do something about it, as in Alfredo Jaar's documentation of the massacres of Rwanda; but also to be moved by beauty and wonder, as in Danica Dakić's film *Grand Organ*. As Alfredo Jaar has noted: 'if images lose their power to affect us, we have lost our humanity' (page xx).

The relation of our senses and their 'sensations' to our minds and their 'feelings' has been a continuous field of enquiry in the history of philosophy and of art. The 'authenticity', 'signature', 'expression' that leave traces in a sensible medium (whether paint, film, built space, computer animation, poetry, music etc.) are instruments in the hands of artists that will not disappear. Craft – skill with materials – is sometimes marginalised, although it has found a powerful advocate recently in the writings of sociologist Richard Sennett.

As long as we inhabit material bodies (that is, until we lose our senses) the sensual qualities of art will continue to matter. A relation between the artist's sensibilities, the sensual quality of the artwork, and their combined impact on the viewer is here evident in work by Nicholas Hlobo, Carol Rama, Otto Muehl, Magdalena Abakanowicz, and painters in *The Human Stain*.

The best art touches us in all three: the head, heart and hand – mind, body and spirit. A whole art appealing to the whole person.

A criticism levelled both at skill with materials and at 'expression' in art has been that these qualities can disguise a lack of intellectual rigour. Narcissism and emotional self-indulgence are never attractive (or successful) in art or life. As Raymond Pettibon remarks: 'It's a mistake to assume about any of my work that it's my own voice. Because that would be the most simple-minded ineffective art that you can make'. *Touched* is an invitation to consider the role of affect in art, but more urgently it's a proposal that the viewer be affected by the art. It affirms that art is a social activity, not a solipsistic one.

The 1970s slogan 'politics of the personal' was a challenge to the contemporary understanding of both those terms – that politics was insufficiently reflective of society, and that individuals could be activists. Carolee Schneemann's *Interior Scroll* 1975 (Tate Collection) is a beautiful reminder of the battle of feminists and other groups to change the 'dominant culture'. Schneemann lists the attributes of the art she loves, banned by 'mainstream' structuralist art critics and artists of that time: 'Emotion' is first on the list, followed by 'Intuition, Inspiration, Spontaneity, Personal Clutter, The Persistence of Feelings, The Hand–Touch Sensibility...' More than thirty years on, you can hear the anger in Schneemann's litany, and anger is a good place to start any political action. 'I think anger is ... the first political emotion. It is often anger that moves the subject to action. Anger is the emotion that produces motion, the mood that moves the subject.'[1]

One of the most powerful tools of the 'minority activists' who helped to shift modernism into postmodernism was the revival of the human body as a site of social and political significance; the notion of 'embodiment' became critical and has remained so. But since the 1990s, globalisation has created the additional need for an urgent reconsideration of the local. The concept of emplacement results from adding to embodiment its context of locality, history, specificity. Embodiment implies integration of mind and body; emplacement suggests the sensuous interrelationship of body–mind–environment.

The ambition of *Touched*, then, is not simply to affect the social but to extend the concept of the social towards emplacement. We've chosen artists whose work reaches out to mind, body and soul – to the critical intellect, the

senses and the emotions – art that addresses not only the whole person but the whole context of experience in which it is apprehended. This includes, but is more than, a phenomenological approach, grounded in the senses. It also invokes memory, history, geography, time passing: emplacement.

The last word goes to Michael Hardt and Antonio Negri: 'All the theoretical elements we have accumulated thus far in our discussion ... despite all their power, risk lying inert beside one another without one more element that pulls them together and animates them in a coherent project. What is missing is love. Yes, we know that term makes many readers uncomfortable ... We think instead that love is an essential concept for philosophy and politics, and the failure to interpret and develop it is one central cause of the weakness of contemporary thought.'[2]

Lewis Biggs

1 Simon Critchley, *Infinitely Demanding: Ethics of Commitment, Politics of Resistance* (London: Verso, 2007)

2 *Commonwealth* (Cambridge, MA: Harvard University Press, 2009), p. 79.

Rosa Barba

Free Post Mersey Tunnels, 2010

4

Pipes, sound, ventilator
Courtesy Carlier I Gebauer, Berlin and Galleria Gió Marconi, Milan
New commission for Liverpool Biennial 2010, *Touched*

What does subterranean Liverpool sound like? Rosa Barba brings the underground energy of Liverpool to our attention by capturing its visceral sound and conveying it through an intricate sculptural labyrinth of pipes, bringing the inside out and the underneath up, and making audible (and even visible) the inner life of the city's underworld.

This low-tech industrial landscape, an organic design enriched by a thick patina as if long subjected to the transformations of entropic processes, enters and exits the exhibition space, channelling the recorded noise of the traffic and the ventilation towers of the tunnels that carry trains and road vehicles under the river Mersey. The installation concludes in a resonant sculptural conglomeration from which issues a concert of disarticulated, mechanical sounds.

The peristalsis of the noisy cavity of the city's belly acts as a metaphor for its organic, almost human, functionality. In fact, the idea is precisely to create an analogy between the body of the city and that of a living entity, taking an internal viewpoint in order to explore its primeval self (its gut feelings as 'the unexpressed').

Rosa Barba's work often unveils (rather than concealing) its mechanical / technical components. This exposure allows us to see behind the world of appearances, manifesting the theatricality somehow implicit in both life and art. By showing the 'mechanism' in this way, the artist confers a humanised vulnerability on her constructed imagery. Seduced and intrigued by the apparent simplicity of her low-tech devices, the viewer is captivated and gently forced outside the comfort zone of a single standpoint.

Barba is able to give voice to the lyricism that equally permeates the brutality of the natural and constructed landscapes. She reinterprets Romanticism anew, by placing herself in a position equally distant from a sentimentalist account of affection and from the machismo of the industrialised world.

Lorenzo Fusi

Supported by

Mersey Tunnels, Liverpool stamped envelope

Historical image of Mersey tunnel under construction from *The Mersey Tunnel*, officially named Queensway, Mersey Tunnel Joint Committee, Liverpool, p. 50

© Rosa Barba

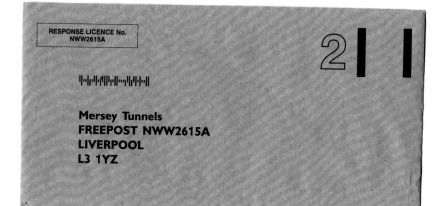

Mersey Tunnels
FREEPOST NWW2615A
LIVERPOOL
L3 1YZ

EXCAVATION OF DUMPLING IN JUNCTION CHAMBER.

Tania Bruguera and selected artists from *Cátedra Arte de Conducta*

Series of artworks, happenings and events newly commissioned for *Touched*

Tania Bruguera's performances and social interventions question and subvert the connections between art and life. Frequently, she requires the viewer to cross the boundaries that conventionally define the role of the audience and that of the artist, and so question their own relationship to the politics of creative expression.

For instance, when uniformed policemen on horseback herded visitors into the centre of the Tate Modern Turbine Hall in the 2008 performance *Tatlin's Whispers*, it was the audience's subservience that created the artwork. Similarly, Bruguera's infamous 2009 performance in Bogotá involved offering free cocaine to an audience listening to a panel discussion on the possibilities for heroism under the current circumstances in Colombia. Her interest in the response and participation of the audience does not exempt the artist herself from the responsibilities of political art, even envisioning its most extreme consequences: the artist's own death (noticeably in the piece *Autosabotage* devised for *The Fear Society* during the 2009 Venice Biennale).

In 2002, Bruguera initiated *Cátedra Arte de Conducta*, the first performance and time-based art studies programme in Latin America devoted to political art. According to the artist, this alternative art school was designed to explore 'the way in which ethics, ideology and history intertwine with memory, sociology,

history of art'. The *Cátedra*, an enterprise now concluded, promoted a new generation of political artists whose international recognition is the most important result of Bruguera's initiative. The former participants (now artists in their own right) will work in Liverpool around two themes: the utopian city and Allan Kaprow's cultural and artistic legacy. These two apparently separate topics are in fact linked through their mutual aims: they attempt to 'touch' the city; they deconstruct and question the traditional notion of museum (as the only physical and mental space where art can be presented, consumed and produced); and they cut across the demarcation lines that separate politics, art and life.

Bruguera and Lorenzo Fusi jointly selected the participants committed to this collective experiment of institutional critique: Ana Olema Hernández Matamoro, Ariel Orozco Rodriguez, Carlos Martiel, Reynier Leyva Novo, Lavastida Cordovi Hamlet, Jeanette Chavez Ruiz, Jesus Hernandez Hernandez, James Roger Bonachea Guerra, José Fidel García Valenzuela, La Vaughn Belle, Levi Enrique Orta Mendoza, Loidys Carnero Pineda, Núria Güell Serra, Omni-Zonafranca (group), Yaima Carrazana Ciudad, Yali Romagosa Sanchez, and Bram Kaprow.

Lorenzo Fusi

Anibal López lecturing at the *Cátedra Arte de Conducta*

Song Dong
Touching the People, 2010

Performance, modified video projection, documentation footage

The work of Chinese artist Song Dong represents a perfect illustration of the notion of anti-monumentality. His series of public interventions centred on writing poems on street pavements only using a brush and water clearly demonstrates his interest in the ongoing process of the dematerialisation of art. His ephemeral actions imply a titanic effort, but the results thus achieved vanish before the action can be said concluded. The notion of impermanence is a useful conceptual tool for accessing his practice, a notion that becomes most pressing when it is applied to the domain of public art, since its focal point lies in the audience's expectation of physically meeting art and not just ideas.

One of Song Dong's most ambitious projects to date is entitled *Waste Not*, presented at New York's Museum of Modern Art in 2009. This work encompasses almost fifty years of Chinese history by displaying all the purchased items that have come into his mother's home during the last half-century. The piece, based upon the Chinese concept of *wu jin qi yong* (the 'waste not' of the title), translates a strategy of survival into a poetic tribute to personal history, domesticity, familial bonds and

affections. At each presentation the work is reconfigured by the artist with the help of his mother, so that it is a factual collaboration that interestingly challenges the notion of authorship.

Song Dong has also referenced his father through his work and addressed the repression of emotions derived from cultural conventions and social rules, notably in the piece *Touching My Father* (1998), an action and video-projection that narrates the artist's inability to achieve physical (and consequently emotional) proximity to his father. In Chinese culture, physical contact between men of different generations is not socially acceptable. As Song Dong recalls: 'In my mind, I have no memory of touching or hugging my father.' This work exemplifies how very important it is to art and life to dare to touch.

Courtesy of the artist

NS Harsha

Sky Gazers, 2010

4

16 painted wood boards (each 243.7 x 121.8 cm, 1.8 cm thickness – floor component), mirror
Courtesy of the artist
New commission for Liverpool Biennial 2010, *Touched*

With his paintings, site-specific installations and community-based activities, NS Harsha makes social and political commentaries on a range of issues surrounding globalisation, such as migrant labour, media representation and changing notions of cultural heritage. Drawing on Indian craft and painting traditions as well as popular culture, Harsha depicts scenes of everyday life in rural India alongside images of world events. In so doing, his work calls into question the divergence of terms such as 'local' and 'global', 'specific' and 'universal', suggesting, for example, that 'the global is always already located within the local imagination'.

Harsha's sensitive, whimsical and frequently humorous works draw out the interrelations between individual and collective experience, seeking an empathetic engagement with the concerns and anxieties of human existence in a fast-changing world. Particularly in his environments and installations, the artist invites the viewer inside the work, transcending the notion of physical participation and proactively aiming at his/her emotional involvement. The collective 'Us' addressed by Harsha is not a spectacle to look at, but a flow to dive into. The installation devised

for *Touched* is exemplary of this. The separation between the viewer and the viewed is challenged by the audience being integrated with the image. By entering a space constellated by a multitude of star-gazers, one is invited to second their meditative and lyric observation of an imaginary sky. In so doing, the 'I' becomes 'We' and the expression of individual wishes and desires is transformed into a communal act. The projection of our expectations and hopes is reflected by a mirrored ceiling, which suggests that whatever happens in future – rather than being dictated by faith, destiny or other uncontrollable forces – mainly lies in our own hands.

Although we all experience, at those times when our sense of inadequacy and finite capacity are most evident, a similar fascination for spirituality, the answer to our uncertainties (the artist seems to suggest) cannot be found anywhere but in the reflection of our own gaze, acting as a gate open to the intimacy of our selves.

Lorenzo Fusi

Supported by

Victoria Miro

Alfredo Jaar
The Marx Lounge, 2010

4

Mixed media installation
Courtesy of the artist and Galerie Lelong
New commission for Liverpool Biennial 2010, *Touched*

Alfredo Jaar's work considers some of recent history's most traumatic events and the implications of how these are communicated. For *Touched*, he presents two works that reflect on the legacies and status of humanist thinking and the ongoing problems of how to articulate, document and commemorate human suffering.

Comfortably furnished for lounging, and painted in rallying red, *The Marx Lounge* is situated conceptually between a library reading room and the seamier environs of a public boudoir. As the plethora of recent symposia, publications and exhibitions attests, Karl Marx's pivotally influential ideas continue to be recalibrated. In part, this can be attributed to the current economic crisis, but it also reflects wider discussions within contemporary cultural and critical theory that seek to fundamentally interrogate and rethink the capitalist system. Responding to this upsurge of interest, *The Marx Lounge* presents a platform for audiences to access an extensive archive of reading material focusing on Marx's political, economic, humanitarian and philosophical ideas.

The Marx Lounge includes recent publications provided by the UK's primary radical publishing company, Verso Books, and copies of *The Communist Manifesto* translated into the minority languages of Liverpool. Activating the work is a lively discursive programme of talks and discussions by leading thinkers in the field and an accompanying poster campaign on public sites around the city.

The Marx Lounge is a complete experiential environment where audiences can sit, read, speculate and come to their own conclusions on the relevance and viability of Marx's ideas today.

In addition, Alfredo Jaar presents a new three-channel video work, *We Wish to Inform You that We Didn't Know*, in the old Scandinavian Hotel building. Please see p. 66 for further information.

Frances Loeffler

Project Sponsor

Everyone talks about the weather. We don't., 1968
Sozialistische Deutsche Studentenbund
(Socialist German Student Union)

Poster designed by Ulrich Bernhardt and Jürgen Holtfreter
Collection of Alfredo Jaar

Alle reden vom Wetter.

Wir nicht.

SDS SOZIALISTISCHER DEUTSCHER STUDENTENBUND

Allan Kaprow

Recognized as the father of Happenings, American artist Allan Kaprow (1927–2006) was also a cultural critic and lifelong educator who steered numerous generations of students into a style of art making that was simultaneously cerebral, utopian, political, improvisational, and infused with wit.

After an early career as a painter under the tutelage of Hans Hoffmann, Kaprow moved during the late 1950s and 1960s toward impermanent interactive Environments and participatory events, which often featured ordinary activities taking place in everyday spaces.

Kaprow wrote that the line between art and life should be kept as fluid, and perhaps indistinct, as possible, implicitly questioning the way in which the art of the museums and market is produced and consumed.

In considering the theme of *Touched*, Kaprow's Happenings are events intrinsically linked to the public domain, and their physicality is important too when considering how art may touch the city. An event that causes change: that produces a chain-reaction of other events.

Kaprow's work has been exhibited and performed extensively in the United States and internationally. It is this legacy and the possibility of personal re-inventions of his work that the artists of the Cátedra Arte De Conducta and Tania Bruguera are asked to consider.

Each week throughout the biennial, two artists from the Cátedra will re-invent a written score from Kaprow's archive, with an opening act or action every Wednesday afternoon 16.00–18.00.

The following works will be reinvented: *Self Service* (1966); *Transfer* (1968); *Round Trip* (1968); *Six Ordinary Happenings: Shape and Charity* (1969); *Words* (1962); *Time Pieces* (1973); *Affect* (1974); *Match* (1975); *Satisfaction* (1976); *Mediation1, (zazen)* (1981); *Office Boy* (1987).

Amanprit Sandhu

We would like to thank Hauser and Wirth and the Allan Kaprow Estate for their support.

Affect, 1974

Photos illustrating how to perform *Affect* from the Activity booklet
2 Measures
published by Martano Editore, Turin, Italy, 1974
Courtesy Allan Kaprow Estate and Hauser & Wirth

Photos: Bee Ottinger

Ryan Trecartin
Trill-ogy Comp, 2009

HD video, mixed media installation
Courtesy of the artist and Elizabeth Dee Gallery, New York

Ryan Trecartin is at the forefront of a generation of artists using video and digital media to new aesthetic and critical ends. His work borrows from and expertly manipulates the languages and forms of popular culture to create densely layered video narratives presented within highly sculptural and theatrical settings.

Presented in the UK for the first time, *Trill-ogy Comp* (2009) comprises three works: *K-CoreaINC.K (section a)*, *Sibling Topics (section a)*, and *P.opular S.ky (section ish)*. Featuring a cast of family and friends (in particular long-time collaborator Lizzie Fitch) and the artist himself, these works are characterised by a feverishly high-pitched, fast-paced style and the constant negotiation of notions of narrative, gender and belonging. Their dominant themes revolve around consumerism, youth culture and the complete fragmentation of identity in a world where personae are continuously multiplied and erased, downloaded and over-written.

The films radiate the kind of wired energy you might feel after a long night surfing the net, and are shaped by the characteristics and aesthetics of the Internet. While each component part is tediously mass-produced, made up of Ikea furniture and TV show one-liners, the possibilities this world presents lie in the non-formulaic. Nothing is fixed, but everything is always re-calibrating into new forms. There is no single point of view. Characters address themselves in the second and third person. Nor is there a singular sense of self. Objects and persons merge, transmogrify and become one another. Identity is performed *in situ*, as much defined by the scenography as by any inherent character traits. For *Touched*, the films are presented as immersive installations in the sprawling, labyrinthine basement of a former hardware store (the building, said to have the longest shop front in Britain, runs almost the entire length of a street). Moving through and between the interconnected rooms, viewers become part of the artist's transitional world.

Trill-ogy Comp doesn't so much 'touch' in the gentle sense as pull you in, shake you up, utterly absorb you, and then set you down, reeling. The works are visually, aurally and emotionally assaulting, leaving our senses disrupted and our thought processes open to new perspectives on the world.

Frances Loeffler

Still from *Sibling Topics (section a)*, 2009
HD video, 51 min 26 sec
Courtesy of the artist and Elizabeth Dee Gallery, New York

Re:Thinking Trade

52 Renshaw Street, L1 4PN
Tel: 0845 220 2800   www.biennial.com
Open: daily 10.00–18.00
Free Entry   Fully Accessible

Since the social activism of the 1960s, many artists have taken a critical stance towards the dominant consumerism of 'advanced' societies. Bypassing, resisting or intervening in the mechanisms of late capitalism, they have sought to make socially relevant art that works outside or against the constraints of consumerism, bringing producer and consumer back into a human relationship.

As a distinct themed section within *Touched*, *Re:Thinking Trade* proposes to 'touch' the city where it has been affected by globalisation with a suite of commissions that reappropriate the transactions of everyday economies. Artworks will offer 'customers' a variety of alternative ways to trade their time and attention in exchange for a benefit. This may be tangible, a real product, or it may be more ethereal and impalpable: an intellectual or emotional device to touch the recipient's general well-being or self-perception.

The artists in this grouping have been selected for their interest in critically rethinking systems of trade and exchange. However, theirs is not so much an antagonistic critique of these systems as a reframing of the act of economic transaction. By providing services, which

are of real benefit to individuals, they seek to reclaim individuality from the anonymity and indifference of standard systems of economic exchange and to recover the reciprocity, generosity and human gestures remaining between individuals in the reciprocal acts of production and consumption.

The negotiation between an artwork and its audience already encapsulates a basic economic principle: I give you something in exchange for something you give me. Art has to offer a broad range of emotions, affect and vision, the cost of which would be high if translated into monetary terms. An event such as a biennial does not provide or disperse this value for free. One can instead say that such events are highly demanding, since they ask for what is most valuable in contemporary life: attention, acknowledgement and time. *Re:Thinking Trade* is a hub for the alternative transaction of ideas, experiences and ultimately of 'humanity', envisioning new ways to trade people's time and attention with artworks that seek out the possibilities for a virtuous process of economic exchange.

Lorenzo Fusi

Photograph: Alex Wolkowicz

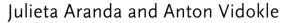

Julieta Aranda and Anton Vidokle

Time/Bank, 2009–ongoing

4

Mixed media installation

Over the last decade, Julieta Aranda and Anton Vidokle, alongside numerous collaborators, have produced a wide range of innovative international initiatives that critically reposition the dominant models of art's production and distribution. These include e-flux, a web-based resource, publishing and distribution facility that also stages a number of special projects such as unitednationsplaza; a free year-long school based in Berlin, EVR (e-flux video rental); and Night School, a temporary school at the New Museum in New York City.

For *Touched*, Aranda and Vidokle are opening the very first branch of *Time/Bank*, an initiative drawing on their longstanding interest in autonomous practices and circulation mechanisms. *Time/Bank* was launched in the summer of 2010 as an online platform that allows participants to trade their time, knowledge and skills, rather than acquire goods and services through the use of money. *Time/Bank* invites artists, curators, critics, activists, theorists and other cultural practitioners to request, offer and pay for services in *Time/Bank* hours. When an individual performs a task, he or she earns credit hours that may be banked for use at a later date, donated to another person or contributed to *Time/Bank* for the development of communal projects.

A little different in appearance from a conventional bank branch, the Liverpool *Time/Bank* branch includes an exhibition of time-currency prototypes designed by a range of international artists and the *Time/Bank* office – a flexible space where visitors can open a *Time/Bank* account and engage with the bank's activities.

For further information please visit the Liverpool Biennial website at www.biennial.com and the e-flux *Time/Bank* at http://www.e-flux.com/timebank

Frances Loeffler

time/bank

Karmelo Bermejo

The Grand Finale. Bank Loan Granted to an Art Gallery Used to Pay a Firework Display at the Closing Ceremony of Art Basel Miami Beach, 2009

HD Video transferred to Blu-Ray, 2 min 29 sec.
Courtesy of the artist and Galeria Maisterra Valbuena, Madrid

Karmelo Bermejo's work often references commerce, labour and economic exchange. The inclusion of his work in the *Re:Thinking Trade* exhibition, which aims at imagining alternative methods of trade, should consequently come as no surprise.

The series, entitled *Contribution of Labor Free of Charge to...*, is exemplary in illustrating the artist's interest in economy-related issues and in reversing or undermining conventional economics. This body of works is based upon actions carried out by the artist who, without being asked or remunerated, freely performed various tasks on behalf of commercial enterprises. Bermejo (by cleaning the tables of a Burger King restaurant, the windows of a Deutsche Bank branch or the display vitrines of a Gucci retailer) subverts the notion of exploitation, metaphorically reattributing to the weakest and most vulnerable strata of society authority and free will in their processes of decision-making. Once these humble forms of labour are provided voluntarily, instead of being poorly paid, their meaning is elevated to a higher rank in the hierarchy of values: they become generous gifts, donations or charitable acts. Paradoxically, the moment the artist gratifies the commercial establishment (i.e. corporate business, banking and the luxury market, all activities that in some way exploit undocumented workers) with unasked gifts of generosity, he empowers those who normally perform these duties for little money and reveals the truth of their exploitation.

In Liverpool Karmelo Bermejo presents a video-work entitled *The Grand Finale* (2009). This is the documentation of a pyrotechnic show organised by the artist on the shore of Miami Beach during Basel art fair, culminating in a firework that illuminates a billboard-sized sign bearing the word 'Recession'. The ultimate global threat is celebrated in this artwork, which questions our fears and insecurities related to the consequences of the credit crunch, and ironically comments on the monetary and speculative value created by the international contemporary art market.

Lorenzo Fusi

Minerva Cuevas
Del Montte, 2003–present

Mixed media installation
Courtesy of the artist and kurimanzutto, Mexico City

Minerva Cuevas creates socially and politically engaged interventions, performances, video and photographic works that frequently draw on extensive periods of research. With subtly disruptive gestures, her work mimics – in order to subvert – existing corporate and governmental structures. The ongoing *Mejor Vida Corp* (Better Life Corporation), for example, is a not-for-profit corporation offering free products and services such as subway passes, student ID cards, recommendation letters and lottery tickets. In a systematic act of subversion, *Mejor Vida Corp* 'touches' the dominant models of trade and exchange with gestures of exchange, solidarity and sabotage. In more recent work, the artist's research has led her to investigate alternative trading systems, the oil industry in Mexico and the concept of social ecology.

For Cuevas's presentation in *Re:Thinking Trade*, colourful billboard-style murals form a backdrop to an arrangement of objects, archival documentation and research materials. These extend the artist's *Del Montte* campaign, a major ongoing series of works that references events in South America's recent political history and the privatisation and misuse of the world's natural resources. Various iterations of this series of works have been staged at a number of exhibition venues internationally. In this instance, Cuevas relates the work to the specific context of Liverpool. With a series of graphic prints that originated in research conducted at Liverpool's Museum of Slavery, she connects the display to the city's former trading networks. In particular, she draws out its extensive links with South American countries.

Situated in a former hardware store's suite of empty window display cases, the work is embedded in the heart of the city, taking place on its streets, for its passers-by and within its commercial networks. And yet the installation defamiliarises the commonplace urban experience. While at first sight nothing seems amiss in this routine display of commercialised goods, closer inspection reveals a subtle reappropriation of branding codes. At the heart of the work lies a pointed commentary on the communication strategies of corporate businesses and the unethical behaviours of large-scale global enterprises.

Frances Loeffler

www.irational.org/mvc
www.minervacuevas.com

NACLA's Latin America & Empire Report, Vol. X, No. 7, September 1976.
Collection of the artist

Vol. X, No. 7, September 1976

NACLA'S
LATIN AMERICA
& EMPIRE REPORT
$1.25

BITTER FRUITS

Freee

Every Shop Window is a Soap Box, 2010

Billboard-sized photographs digitally printed on vinyl, on shop windows

Artists Dave Beech, Andy Hewitt and Mel Jordan form the art collective Freee. Since 2004 they have used a variety of ephemeral interventions or 'viral' media – such as publications, journal articles, posters, T-shirts and the Internet – to raise active critical discussion, confrontation and debate about the nature and function of the public sphere.

For example, in the 2006 work *How to Talk to Public Art*, Freee addressed existing public sculptures with a series of placards carrying slogans such as 'there are no experts on happiness' and 'is it me, or do monarchs have an unfair advantage when it comes to being seen or heard?' Freee's 2008 *Advertising Wants to Convert Our Desire For a Better Life Into A Desire to Buy Something* staged a counter-advertising billboard campaign. Featuring the artists wearing sloganised bandanas carrying a text and covering their faces, the work recolonised the spaces of advertising in order to insert critical messages that called into question the mechanisms of the capitalist system.

For *Re:Thinking Trade*, Freee have created *Every Shop Window is a Soap Box*, which will appear in the front windows of a disused commercial space in Liverpool's city centre. A series of polemical slogans,

the work clearly states its provocative position and demands an active political response from the reader.

In the artists' words:

'Slogans ask for things to change. It is a common misconception today that slogans are authoritarian, illiberal and restrictive. Stokely Carmichael would have never used the slogan "Black is Beautiful" if he thought it simply stated a fact that we could understand without first changing ourselves and the world. The feminist slogan "The Personal is Political", likewise, would only make sense once feminism had transformed our understanding of each of its keywords. If black is already (universally understood as) beautiful then we do not need the slogan "Black is Beautiful", and if the personal is already (secured as) political then we do not need the slogan "The Personal is Political". Slogans do not describe the world, they call up a new world to take its place.'

Frances Loeffler

Photo: Louise Downe

Don't Let the Media Have the Monopoly on the Freedom of Speech, 2007
Poster
Courtesy of the artists

Meschac Gaba
Souvenir Palace, 2010

4

Mixed media installation
Courtesy of the artist, Michael Stevenson Gallery, Cape Town and Galleria Artra, Milan

In his work, Meschac Gaba uses systems of trade and exchange to highlight, critique and overturn perceived notions of cultural identity. Socially and politically critical and yet lighthearted and humorous, his works focus in particular on the cultural and economic codes of exchange between Africa and the West. His major work, *The Museum of Contemporary African Art*, was a gradually evolving migratory museum complete with shop, restaurant, library and music room. Gaba himself acted as curator and director, as well as cook, fashion designer, librarian and musician. Other works include an intricately crafted miniature city made of sugar, and elaborate wigs sculpted in the form of the West's most iconic buildings, such as the Eiffel Tower and the Empire State building.

For *Re:Thinking Trade*, Gaba creates an open, performative space in which the experience of belonging is continuously transforming: adapted, renegotiated and rearranged. Here, he has created a souvenir 'shop' with a twist. Unlike the tourist stands found at airports and train stations, *Souvenir Palace* displays regular souvenir trinkets alongside the accumulated detritus of everyday life: Union Jack flags and key rings with old footballs, doors, windows and shoes.

This diversity is matched by a corresponding variety of national identities: each object on display is painted in the colours of a different national flag. More than a simple shop, the work functions as a trading post. Visitors are invited to bring along their own items to be painted and swapped for those on display. The work reinstates a sense of personal investment, imagination and fun into the monotonous serialisation and commodification of nationalistic symbols. Rather than relying on souvenirs that are state-sanctioned or mass-produced, here individuals can celebrate their cultural origins as they wish, using items of personal value, or the familiar, everyday objects encountered in the surrounding environment.

In essence, the work offers an alternative, in microcosm, to an established world system. In the *Souvenir Palace*, economic standards are overturned and notions of cultural belonging are not dictated or fixed, but open to reinterpretation, transformation and exchange.

Frances Loeffler

Supported by

Mondriaan Stichting
(Mondriaan Foundation)

Photo: Steven Dobbins

Daniel Knorr
The Naked Corner, 2010

4

Performance
Courtesy of the artist and Galleria Fonti Napoli
New commission for Liverpool Biennial 2010, *Touched*

Daniel Knorr's practice encompasses a broad variety of artistic media, including performance, installation, photography, drawing, sculpture, interactive technologies, text, found and archival material. The artist's interest lies in the materialisation of the art object / phenomenon, and in the process that transforms a mundane item or event into an act of empowerment, self-analysis and recognition. Although strongly led by this conceptual impetus, Knorr's work is nevertheless incredibly 'human'. It refuses to take distance from the audience; in fact, it continuously seeks the audience's reaction, participation and response. The viewer is not only an integral part of the artist's vision, but stands at the epicentre of his interventions.

According to Rein Wolfs (artistic director of the Kunsthalle Fridericianum in Kassel): 'The art of Daniel Knorr stands for a dynamic connection between the conceptual and the performative. It attests to the artist's humanity, wit, dedication and institutional critique.' His inclusion within *Touched* should consequently come as no surprise, given the artist's persistent commitment to creating a zone of contact between the artwork and its viewer.

The action devised for *Touched* follows the trajectory of the *Re:Thinking Trade* section, which aims to reinterpret the modalities that regulate economic exchange, using the same strategies and devices as the market in order to question the economic system from within. Arguably, the economy could be said to be the strongest engine and propeller behind our actions. It informs our daily lives and there is little else that exercises a similar influence on the way we conduct ourselves, including affecting our freedom of speech, as Knorr suggests with *The Naked Corner*. The slogans selected by the artist and transcribed on to the bare skin of live models have been copyrighted by multinational corporations and by the advertising industry. Despite being a part of our daily language, these sentences cannot be used publicly in any way that suggests a financial exchange. By placing these slogans in a former shop window and (symbolically) in a context of trade, Knorr questions the authority of the business world to appropriate language and, ultimately, meaning.

Lorenzo Fusi

Supported by

GOETHE-INSTITUT
MANCHESTER

Photo: Daniel Knorr   Model: Timmy Olsson

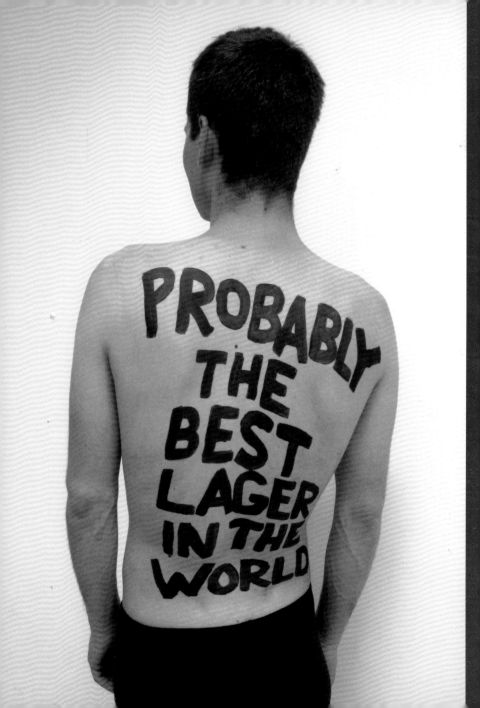

Lee Mingwei
The Mending Project, 2009

4

Interactive installation: 1 10-foot wooden table, 2 wooden chairs, 400 cones of thread
Dimensions variable
Installation at Lombard Freid Projects, New York
Courtesy of the artist and Lombard Freid Projects

Lee Mingwei describes his artistic orientation as 'social conceptualism'. In his participatory works, he invites strangers to join together in simple everyday rituals, such as eating, sleeping, writing letters and engaging in conversation. By staging these highly intimate, personal encounters, the artist creates the potential to build moments of sociability, understanding and trust.

In *The Mending Project*, Lee uses the activity of sewing as a means to draw strangers together in communal encounters. Visitors are asked to bring items of clothing that need mending and sit with the artist while he darns these at their side. Rather than restoring or hiding the tear in the cloth – as a tailor usually would – he celebrates it with a vivid rainbow-like embroidery stitched from brightly coloured threads. In this way, he offers a counterpoint to the throwaway mentality of the modern world. Rather than mere commodities to be discarded when no longer needed, clothes are here reinstated as objects invested with great personal value, their fabrics interwoven with memories of the past. During the course of the exhibition, the mended garments accumulate, the material remnants of a series of fleeting conversations, stories, memories and thoughts.

Hemmed in by tailor's curtains to create an atmosphere of intimacy and calm, *The Mending Project* creates a welcome respite from the humdrum noise of the street and the loneliness experienced by many people living in modern cities. At the heart of this work is the desire to re-instigate moments of closeness and shared understanding between strangers. In life, these moments sometimes occur when people waiting in a queue, or standing at the bus stop, catch each other's eye, unexpectedly smile at one another, or strike up a conversation. They are the moments of recognition and connection between individuals that can make life meaningful, but that are frequently lost in the impersonal transactions that take place in supermarkets, malls and other large-scale shopping venues.

Lee will be on site for the first two weeks of *Touched*, after which time he will pass the role on to other menders who will carry out the work for the duration of the exhibition.

Frances Loeffler

Photo: Anita Kan

The Human Stain: Six Degrees of Separation between the City and the Intimacy of the Self

52 Renshaw Street, L1 4EN
Tel: 0845 220 2800   www.biennial.com
Open: daily 10.00–18.00
Free Entry   Fully Accessible

Since the late 1950s, a plethora of urban anthropologists, sociologists, urban planners, cultural geographers and historians have focused their attention on how our existences are affected by the social texture and infrastructures that have remodelled and informed the notion of 'the city' in contemporary terms (the 'de-industrialised' and the 'post-modernist' cities being particularly relevant cases at hand).

The transformations of the human ecology in these realms constitute the core matter of this section of the exhibition. With *The Human Stain* we are not looking at the macro-representations of these phenomena, but are trying to deconstruct their meaning, breaking it down to the finite experience of the individual.

In recent times we have become accustomed to public art in the context of 'representational cities'[1] – a methodological approach according to which 'messages encoded in the environment are read as text'.[2] The all-embracing and inter-disciplinary methodology derived from this approach, although undeniably useful for framing and narrating the city in its complexity, nevertheless seems to fail in convincingly depicting the individual/personal sphere.

The artists included in *The Human Stain* address the Foucauldian idea that 'corporeal resistance produces subjectivity, not in an isolated or independent way but in a complex dynamic with the resistances of other bodies'.[3] Nonetheless these practitioners start from the individual body and its corporeal presence in order to investigate this chain-reaction of correlated resistances. Ultimately, the selected paintings represent 'the resistance and struggle' necessary to the production of subjectivity, central not only to the sabotage and subversion of current forms of power, but also to 'the constitution of alternative forms of liberation'.[4]

We devised this part of *Touched* as a visual and emotional journey that progressively moves in the direction of the inner labyrinths of the Self. We proceed by degrees of approximation, penetrating the different layers that separate the notion of collectivity from the Freudian Id, that is to say, the rioting sphere of the unexpressed or repressed Self.

These six degrees are envisioned as short stories that can be read either in a continuous narrative line or separately. Each step of this journey towards the intimacy of the Self is named after a book that somehow suggests an atmosphere or state of mind.

Their sequence unfolds as follows:
The Cement Garden (Zbyněk Sedlecký)
Confessions of a Public Speaker (Oren Eliav)
One, No one and One Hundred Thousand (Aime Mpane, Y. Z. Kami)
The Anatomy of Melancholy (Edi Hila)
The Seed of Lost Souls (Tim Eitel)
Naked Lunch (Csaba Kis Róka, Markus Schinwald)

Lorenzo Fusi

1   Jane M. Jacobs, 'The City Unbound: Qualitative Approaches to the City', *Urban Studies*, 30.4–5 (1993), pp. 827–48
2   Setha M. Low (ed.), *Theorizing the City: the New Urban Anthropology Reader* (New Jersey: Rutgers University Press, 2005 [1999]), p. 4
3   Michael Hardt and Antonio Negri, *Commonwealth* (Cambridge, MA: The Belknap Press of Harvard University Press, 2009), p. 31.
4   Ibid.

Oren Eliav
Summon, 2008

Oil on canvas, 120 x 150 cm
All works courtesy of the artist and Braverman Gallery, Tel Aviv

Oren Eliav is an Israeli painter whose work is still little known outside his home country. His paintings are richly layered and insistently worked. In each canvas the pigments melt in a dense succession of sediments. Eliav maintains that his paintings remain incomplete until his characters – or rather, 'visitors' – ultimately come to life. Their ability to hold our attention becomes clear only after a long time of gestation. Allowing each image to emerge from the two-dimensional realm of the canvas is a time-consuming process: a cycle that ends positively only when these ghostly presences finally find a voice of their own. The artist's fascination for a certain disquieting beauty is evident in all his production. While Oren Eliav is certainly interested in ornament and decoration (both almost taboo in contemporary art), the phantoms he depicts are instead primarily committed to telling stories, almost notwithstanding the artist's own intentions.

The series of paintings selected for *The Human Stain* section of *Touched* show the true colours of several public personae.

Men – captured in embarrassing, at times demonic, poses – populate his canvases, unveiling the dark side of politics and the psychological viciousness that lies behind most public appearances.

Eliav's relation to art history is evident. He looks at the legacy of well-regarded Western masters, reinterprets their compositions and mimics their voices; but most similarities dissolve on closer inspection. The apparent familiarity of his imagery strategically engages the viewer in what seems a harmless game. The seductive easiness of his gesture encourages proximity in order to then undermine conventionality and challenge the viewer's expectations. But most importantly, it facilitates a psychological survey of the Other that paradoxically leads to a self-analytical introspection. By getting to know more about his characters, he enables us to achieve a sharp consciousness and self-awareness.

Lorenzo Fusi

Supported by

Also showing

Untitled, 2007
Oil on panel, 20 x 50 cm

Untitled, 2004
Oil on canvas, 40 x 30 cm

Untitled, 2007
Oil on canvas, 150 x 120 cm

Untitled, 2007
Oil on canvas, 100 x 100 cm

Tim Eitel

Matratze, 2008

4

Oil on canvas, 220 x 210 cm
Sammlung Essl, Klosterneuburg/Wien
Courtesy Galerie EIGEN + ART, Leipzig/Berlin and The Pace Gallery, New York

Tim Eitel's name is generally associated with the New Leipzig School, named after the eponymous celebrated art academy. The School, a movement originating during the 1990s in East Germany, consolidated over the course of the last decade and has now achieved international recognition.

Throughout his career the artist has been exploring different pictorial genres, variously concentrating his attention on isolated or small groups of figures, natural and built landscapes and interior spaces. Although Eitel considers painting as a counterpart to the fast consumption of media-generated aesthetics, he is nevertheless interested in understanding what type of images are retained by our minds from the overwhelming flood of mass communications, especially if they are associated with powerful affects, such as fear or desire.

Eitel's process generally starts with a photographic documentation of his surroundings. During this phase he crystallises his impressions by taking snapshots of compositions that unexpectedly attract his attention. He then extracts selected elements from each photograph that, once isolated from the rest of the context, become the core matter of his pictorial investigation. The sense of abandonment, alienation and estrangement achieved by means of this selective process creates a poetic tension between the 'reality' initially photographed and its meticulous pictorial de-contextualisation. Eitel's almost Caravaggesque depictions of the human-scape that populates the least noticeable parts of the city are at once moving and detached. They refuse to indulge in any form of pietism and resist shifting into pure political propaganda.

The three large paintings presented in *The Human Stain* section of *Touched* are powerful exemplars for the artist's research: abandoned mattresses, garbage, supermarket trolleys and a desolate humanity are recurrent themes in his analytical depictions. The anti-heroic penumbra that permeates his work and dwells in his canvases addresses a defeated society. There is no paternalistic or patronising attitude in his attempt to capture beauty in this derelict underworld. Rather, by isolating and elevating to sovereignty in his paintings precisely what we try to remove from our sight, the artist embraces an empathetic vision that refrains from expressing judgement.

Lorenzo Fusi

Supported by

GOETHE-INSTITUT
MANCHESTER

Edi Hila

La Mamma, 2002

4

Acrylic on canvas
82 x 101.5 cm
All works courtesy of the artist

Edi Hila's career spans several decades, a period during which he has managed to survive political disillusion, persecution and censorship. The 1970s were a particularly difficult period for the artist, when he was forbidden from painting by the secret police serving the Albanian Communist dictatorship. His work was seen as being too 'impressionist' and not conforming to the image the country wanted to project internally and abroad. The specific painting that caused Hila most problems looks rather innocent today, especially to those without personal experience of Socialist totalitarianism. The gentle Fauvism of the picture was rejected by the political class, who were offended by Hila's omission of the feet of his figures (this was interpreted as an attempt to destabilise the system). The artist was consequently ostracised.

The country's transition to capitalism has been equally traumatic and destabilising. Hila – unable, like many Albanians, to adjust efficiently to the aggression of the new political system and conform to the anti-idealism of the free market – has become even more introverted. The poetic portrait of the artist's mother entitled La Mamma exemplifies Hila's desire to withdraw from public discussion and the political arena. It nevertheless comments on the social injustices of the capitalist period. In the solitude of her apartment, the woman is captured by the painter in a feeble daily gesture, operating her TV remote control. The image clearly shows that her entire world is bound up in her domestic life, a microcosm that keeps her safe and protected.

After the end of the Communist regime and the reintroduction of the right to private property, most flats and houses in Albania were claimed back by their former owners. As often happens when such a drastic change occurs, bribery and corruption governed the process of reinstating private property. The new landlords quickly proved to be not very compassionate towards the occupiers of the formerly nationalised accommodation. As a result, the weakest strata of society lost the little they had – including the artist's mother, who was forced out of her own apartment. Abruptly and forcibly uprooted from the familiarity of her flat, the woman passed away soon after. Poignantly, the portrait encapsulates both the end of an era and that of a life.

Lorenzo Fusi

Also showing

Casa con antenne,
2009
Oil on canvas
99 x 163 cm

L'attesa alla fermata,
2009
Oil on canvas, 116 x 176 cm

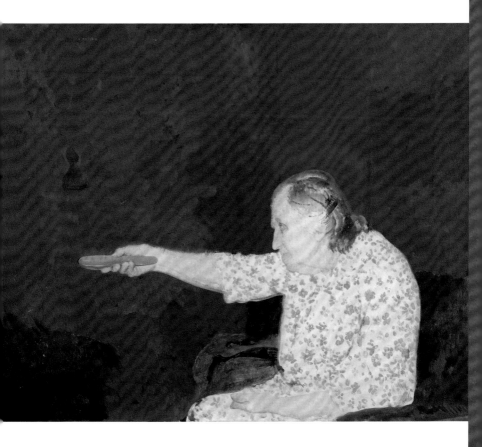

Y. Z. Kami

Dry Land, 1999–2004

Iris-printed photographs with oil painting on paper, 340 x 752 cm
Painting consists of 56 panels
Courtesy of the artist and Gagosian Gallery, New York

4

Educated in Paris – where he studied philosophy – and California, Y. Z. Kami has worked in a variety of media (including photography, installation and sculpture), although he is mainly regarded as a painter. It was his large-scale portraits that first gained him acclaim from the international art world, leading to invitations to show his work in various important exhibitions and biennials.

His work often combines the personal and the political, alternatively shaping an emotional survey of an entire collective body or dwelling on more intimate and private investigation. The artist is not interested in depicting caricatures, over-exposed or exaggerated representations of the Self.

Kami's tone is calm, avoiding commotion or a 'pornographic' exposure of affect and intimacy. Even his deepest investigations retain a certain lightness of touch, an emphatic gentleness that nevertheless bonds the artist to the sitter in a profound and respectful reciprocal tie. According to Kami, in fact, the lengthy process of painting a face is like interiorising it, a form of assimilation.

His paintings are vaporous, almost evanescent, and dissimulate the effort needed to achieve such a casual and natural effect. The mist of light that envelops his imagery is nearly mystical, and creates an aura around his subjects that enables them to escape mundane contingencies in favour of a sort of spiritual elevation.

The selection for *The Human Stain* is focused on a collective portrait almost eight metres wide. In a single visual stream the artist maps the silent relations that connect people to place. *Dry Land* mixes photographs of dilapidated buildings in Detroit with portraits of weary or meditative-looking people. His melancholic – yet lyrical – gaze highlights the people's pride and dignity notwithstanding the desperation and desolation of the photographed environment. Although the faces do not actually 'belong' to the buildings (since the architectural photographs were taken in Detroit, and those of the people in Harlem, New York), yet the work expresses perfectly the notion of 'emplacement'. The mere fact that it is a collage of diverse memories and not a survey of a single site does not undermine the visual cohesion of the cross-references and emotional interrelations highlighted by the whole picture.

Lorenzo Fusi

Aimé Mpane
Ici on crève, 2006–2008

4

Pigment on wood
Series of 50 panels, each one 30 x 30 cm
Collection of the artist, courtesy of Skoto Gallery, New York

Aimé Mpane's work focuses primarily on the legacy of colonialism on the African continent. By linking past and present in a visually cohesive narration, the artist encompasses almost two centuries of socio-political struggle. The history of his home town Kinshasa – formerly known as the 'City of Leopold' (Leopoldville) – is emblematic in this sense. To this day, the memory of the brutalities instigated during the nineteenth century by Leopold II, King of Belgium, is still vivid for the Congolese people; the scar left by his violent occupation is painfully visible on the skin of the indigenous population.

Although these atrocities resound in Mpane's art, he does not suggest self-pity as a tool for change; awareness, solidarity and collective consciousness are more appropriate. The artist's sculptural installation entitled *Congo: Shadow of the Shadow* (2005) is a perfect example. A standing figure made of 4,652 matchsticks – transparent and fragile – pensively looks at a wooden silhouette of a dead man that lies flat at his feet, as if it were a gravestone. His silent presence is not only meditating on the past but also proactively thinking forward, following the long shadow projected onto the floor.

Mpane's work is charged with history and emotions and 'touches' us at different levels. It acts as a reminder, a tool of collective empowerment and a quest for individual memory. The collective portrait selected for *The Human Stain* section of *Touched* includes over fifty rough-cut wood panels. The artist plays with the tactility of each material, following its nature and highlighting its expressive potential. The resulting portraits are acute psychological investigations. The spontaneity of the brushstrokes recalls the lively style of hand-painted signage associated with stereotyped imagery of African villages. The wood panels are often burnt, broken or perforated and the colour adjusts accordingly. The exploration of the material (an investigation carried out beyond the surface of the painting) allows Mpane to enter the psyche and emotional locus of the people and, more broadly, it enables the artist to narrate the history of an entire place.

Lorenzo Fusi

Csaba Kis Róka
Dynamism of Love, 2010

Oil on canvas, 40 x 30 cm
All works courtesy of the artist

Csaba Kis Róka explores the innermost corners of the collective subconscious, delving into the realm of the unexpressed, and blatantly opposing political correctness. Playing with a rich pictorial texture that densely coagulates on his canvases, the artist stages traditional genre scenes imbued with irony, cruelty, abuse and random violence.

Kis Róka's paintings analyse the effects of trauma, social stigmatisation and political repression, and address the conditioning of the individual psyche by the system. The powers that define notions such as shame, depravity and contempt can be traced both allegorically and explicitly in his work: most noticeably when he includes in his compositions men wearing military uniforms or bureaucrats' hats. The governance of the state and the army are the most obvious expressions of manipulation of the Self. Wise old men (resembling the busts of ancient philosophers, alluding critically to conservative education and the legacy of cultural traditions) are also often included in his bestiary. Their bodies are frequently mutilated: a leg is missing or an arm, as in ancient statuary.

Most of his characters suffer as much violence as they perform; the good are indistinguishable from the bad. As in Petronius' *Satyricon*, homosexuality and the tension generated by the difference in age and status of the lovers are central themes. But the range of sexual deviations represented is perhaps closer to de Sade's *The 120 Days of Sodom*. Little is left to the imagination. But Kis Róka's work bypasses vulgarity, since it is immediately obvious that this imagery is a grotesque allegory, the hyper-sexualisation of his characters an allusion to the abuse of power.

The picaresque world narrated by the artist confronts us with our inhibitions. It is a comprehensive review of the most opprobrious psychological features. Csaba Kis Róka reinterprets the lessons of the old masters such as Hieronymus Bosch and Francisco de Goya, adding to their legacy a new twist of witticism enshrouded in camp, queer politics, Gothicism, comics-related aesthetic and youth culture. Arguably his work can be viewed as 'touched in the head'. Yet his emotionally dysfunctional characters (oppressed by a variety of societal clichés and expectations) undoubtedly unveil the dark side of the Self in a somewhat playful and ironic way.

Lorenzo Fusi

Also showing

He Was Born Wild, 2010
Oil on canvas, 40 x 30 cm

Eternal Trust, 2010
Oil on canvas, 25 x 40 cm

Everything For Everyone, 2010
Oil on canvas, 45 x 50 cm

Mellow Rape, 2010
Oil on canvas, 68 x 44 cm

Dare To Be Great, 2010
Oil on canvas, 60 x 50 cm

Heroes, 2010
Oil on canvas, 160 x 130 cm

Desire To Nursing, 2010
Oil on canvas, 130 x 160 cm

Markus Schinwald

Baldwin, 2009

Oil on canvas, 80 x 60 cm
Private collection, courtesy of the artist and Galleria Gió Marconi, Milan

The human body plays a central role in the art of Markus Schinwald. The characters he portrays in his films, photographs and – most noticeably – in his paintings are generally constrained by prostheses and mechanical apparatuses. These devices impede any spontaneity in their movements and create a visual short-circuit between the apparent smoothness of their poses, the elegant nonchalance of the sitters and the sense of coercion and violence emanating from these instruments of torture. The prostheses, Schinwald maintains, are particularly unsettling because one cannot decipher their function. Once deprived of an obvious purpose, they become a general metaphor for uneasiness without further clarification. The fact that their meaning or function is uncertain makes them – besides mysterious – disquieting.

Schinwald's analysis of the human psyche manifests the unsaid and stages (and the term could not be more appropriate since he often references theatre and theatricality) the morbid turbulence of the spirit. The artist brings the inside out, and by so doing the tortuous paths of the psychoanalytic Id surface on his canvases. His work confronts the complex relations that inevitably bond sadist and masochist. In his art it is never clear who is performing violence on whom. The message is ambivalent and consequently blurs the separation between the aggressor and his/her victim.

In several cases, the pains suffered by his characters appear somehow to be self-inflicted: almost a desired form of martyrdom or flagellation. They address implicitly the need to expiate affects such as shame, guilt or a sense of inadequacy. Ultimately they allude to social stigma, and comment on the physical and emotional restrictions imposed by societal order and conventions. The tools of social control are often very subtle, and deconstructing their meaning is not a simple task: Schinwald's soft and mysterious tortures represent a poignant allegorical reference to their power.

In *The Human Stain*, Schinwald illustrates one of the darkest and most uncomfortable chapters in this inner journey towards the Self.

Lorenzo Fusi

Supported by

austrian cultural forum[lon]

Also showing

Basil, 2005
Oil on canvas, 64.5 x 54 cm
Private collection
Courtesy of Georg Kargl Fine
Arts, Vienna

Madeleine, 2009
Oil on canvas, 73 x 53 cm
Private collection courtesy of
Galerie Yvon Lambert,
Paris / New York

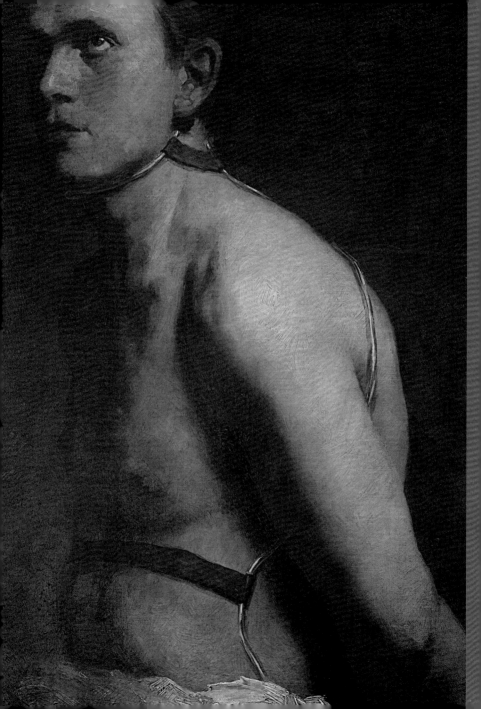

Zbyněk Sedlecký
Staff 2, 2010

4

Acrylic on canvas, 200 x 140 cm
All works courtesy of the artist

Zbyněk Sedlecký generally uses acrylic colours on canvas to create his compositions. His gesture is quick, brushstrokes giving life rapidly to cityscapes where the human presence is often only evoked. The result looks like a sketchbook, an agile collection of transient thoughts. Although large in scale, his images refuse to freeze the moment. They follow the flux and course of history. In fact, these works have the formal quality of a watercolour rather than retaining the 'material and temporal solidity' of a painting on canvas. Transparent and immediate, Sedlecký's ideas are crystallised in a water-diluted form.

Massive silhouettes of brutal buildings (modernist evidence of a Socialist past) witness the transition to the uncertainty of the present and sceptically look at the future. The striking contrast between the harshness of the scenery and the gentleness of the palette generates the internal tension that characterises each painting. Suspended amid disillusion and regret, the artist comments on the role of the individual in a time when no room is left for ideological thinking.

Mimicking the style formerly adopted by the Western bourgeoisie for documenting the marvels of nature and recalling evocative and 'exotic' journeys, Sedlecký's canvas-sized aquarelles are like a pictorial Grand Tour that reinterprets the landscape genre and renegotiates one's own understanding of beauty and the category of Romantic painting. The sense of alienation or uneasiness communicated by his anti-idyllic take on the city is not dictated by a blatant political agenda (although his images are indeed political). It is his sincere interest in form, composition and colour that allows these feelings to show.

More recently, Sedlecký has experimented with collage. The incorporation of common materials such as laminate flooring or linoleum into his work is not aimed at hyper-realism. He instead plays with optical perspective and challenges the viewer's ability to reconstruct the volume of the painted space. The wood panelling inserted in his canvases does not second the normal perspective of the picture, but follows a visual law all its own. The forcible contrast between the painted surface and these mundane elements is not immediately apparent, although it confers on these figurative works an inexplicable sensation of visual rupture.

Lorenzo Fusi

Also showing

Hamburg 1, 2007
Acrylic on canvas,
140 x 200 cm

Vítkovice, 2008
Acrylic on canvas,
200 x 140 cm

Offices, 2008
Acrylic on canvas,
140 x 200 cm

Airport, 2010
Acrylic on canvas,
140 x 200 cm

Laura Belém

The Temple of a Thousand Bells, 2010

17

1000 hand-blown glass bells, nylon string, 5.1 sound system, lighting
Audio duration: 8 min 2 sec
Music by Fernando Rocha
New commission for Liverpool Biennial 2010, *Touched*

Narratives of memory, displacement and transience are central to Laura Belém's context-responsive artworks. Her poetic and meditative interventions touch our emotions, and so cause us to shift our perspectives on the everyday. In her 2004–05 installation *Enamorados* (Enamoured), for example, two rowing boats animated by searchlights continuously signalled to one another across an expanse of water, as if they were lovers engaged in a romantic tryst.

The delicacy of her artistic gesture often contrasts with the gravitas of her subject matter. For instance, *Shipwreck*, a video that shows a drawing of a caravel gradually melting into an indistinct pool of colour, where loss, death and disillusionment are evoked as the image gradually becomes unrecognisable and then disappears. The work refers specifically through the caravel to the colonial occupation of South America, but also acts as a wider metaphor for migration, exile and nostalgia.

Similarly, the installation created for Liverpool focuses on the relations between past and present and introduces the viewer to a new realm of possibilities for the future. It is a free adaptation of an ancient legend, the story of an island temple whose most remarkable and distinctive feature was its endowment of a thousand bells. Allegedly, the sound of these bells could be heard by travellers crossing the sea even at a great distance from the island. Over the centuries, the island sank into the ocean, and so did the temple and its bells. But the island and its shrine are not completely forgotten, as shown by the unremitting attempts of a sailor to hear again the music of the sunken bells. Although their sound has long vanished into the depths of the ocean and his undertaking seems pointless, the man does not give up trying and obsessively pursues his search.

The artist cannot guarantee that the lost music of these bells (possibly symbolising our continuous and somehow frustrated quest for spirituality) will be heard during the exhibition period. But traces of their sound might find a resonance in the ears and hearts of those who are most able to open themselves to their surroundings and interpret silence.

Lorenzo Fusi

Photo: Laura Belém

Supported by

The Henry Moore
Foundation

Emese Benczùr
Think About The Future, 2010

2

Mixed media outdoor installation
New commission for Liverpool Biennial 2010, *Touched*

Emese Benczùr first expressed her concern for the future, as a person and artist, in 1997 when she repeatedly embroidered the sentence 'I think about the future' along strips of fabric into which the phrase 'day by day' had been previously woven. At the beginning of the process the artist had set for herself an ideal lifespan of one hundred years: the task of the project was to embroider by hand the same sentence as many times as there were days still to live in her 'planned' life.

Whereas the sentence 'day by day' is mechanically woven into the fabric strips, the sentence that expresses purposive thinking about the future is instead hand-stitched. Throughout this action, the artist consumes the present time in thinking about her future. Metaphorically speaking, while time is a 'given', the way we use the given time depends on our free will and conscious decisions. The mechanical repetition of time passing (conventionally expressed as a linear measure) is questioned by Benczùr: she undermines the notion of the linear development of time by continuously interjecting her projection of the future into daily experience.

Similarly, for the 2010 Liverpool Biennial, the artist invites the viewer to '*think*

about the future'. The project has been inspired by the shell of a disused cinema, formerly known as The Futurist. The medium of cinema was initially associated intrinsically with the technological achievements of modernity (perfectly encapsulated by the Lumière brothers' *L'Arrivée d'un train en gare à La Ciotat*, the legendary shot of the arrival of a train whose audacious realism allegedly scared to death its nineteenth-century audience), an understanding that failed most precisely to foresee the death of cinema as a collective experience. Emese Benczùr points the finger at the end of an era: in a *Blade Runner*-like scenario of abandoned buildings, there is little room for positivist thinking. If we want to survive oil-spills, the inconsiderate exploitation of natural resources and climate-change-related catastrophes, we must urgently imagine new ways to harvest the *Spectacle of the Everyday* [1].

Lorenzo Fusi

1 Title of the tenth Lyon Biennale, 2009.

Supported by

    LUDWIG MÚZEUM
Kortárs Művészeti Múzeum
Museum of Contemporary Art
www.ludwigmuseum.hu

Emese Benczùr
Day By Day, 1998
Courtesy of the artist

Danica Dakić

Grand Organ, 2010

Single-channel video installation, HD video transferred to Blu-Ray disc, 13 min
Original music by Bojan Vuletić. Director of photography Egbert Trogemann
New commission for Liverpool Biennial 2010, *Touched*

18

Danica Dakić's practice and approach to art-making twisted during the war in Bosnia and the siege of Sarajevo (1992–96). At the time of the conflict Dakić, who had studied painting in Sarajevo and Belgrade and then film and video in Germany, was only remotely – if at all – in touch with her home country, family and friends. In a series of paintings entitled *White Pictures* she translated the sense of loss and disconnection she was then experiencing by devising constructivist-inspired and architecturally structured compositions. These were almost an exercise of self-discipline, as she says, a means for keeping her grounded and steady in a moment of uncertainty.

In 1996, after a period of self-imposed isolation, she presented *Blaues Auge,* an installation comprising thousands of newspaper cuttings concerning the war in Yugoslavia collected over a period of several years. Applied to windows and kept together by a transparent film, the news and images from the war impeded any visual dialogue between the outside and inside of the gallery space. The piece not only highlighted the lack of communication with her motherland throughout the conflict, but suggested the opacity of the information provided by the media. Ever since, although her work can still be arguably defined as pictorial, the artist has gradually abandoned painting in favour of other forms of artistic expression, including video, photography, performance, sound and text.

The artist's *Touched* commission was initially inspired by the majestic organ located in St George's Hall. This polyvalent space, a nineteenth-century *tour de force*, was designed as a court of justice as well as a place for civic leisure and entertainment. Throughout production, Dakić has visually elaborated on the notions of polyphony and childhood, besides investigating the relationships between justice and spectacle, language and music, individuality and collectivity. Solidly bonded to and rooted within local history, pride and heritage, this new video-installation transcends the particularity of the place by bringing to the forefront the element of 'performance' implicit in the legal system. The analogies that the artist conjures between the virtuosi of the law court and the talents expressed by both the composer and the performers act as an allegorical reminder: each one of us is only a key on a board, an isolated note in a much broader composition.

Lorenzo Fusi

Supported by

CALOUSTE
GULBENKIAN
FOUNDATION

GOETHE-INSTITUT
MANCHESTER

Danica Dakić
Grand Organ (production still), 2010
C-print
© Danica Dakić, VG Bild-Kunst, Bonn

Alfredo Jaar

We Wish to Inform You That We Didn't Know, 2010

Three-channel video installation written and directed by Alfredo Jaar
Editing: Jerzy Klebieko and Alfredo Jaar. Cinematography: Alfredo Jaar. Sound: Jerzy Klebieko
Production Assistant: Jordan Benke. Production: Angola 72 Films
New commission for Liverpool Biennial 2010, *Touched*

Alfredo Jaar's work considers some of recent history's most traumatic events and the implications of how they are communicated. For *Touched*, he presents two works that reflect on the legacies and status of humanist thinking and the ongoing problems of how to articulate, document and commemorate human suffering.

We Wish to Inform You That We Didn't Know is a new three-channel video that refers to Jaar's *The Rwanda Project* of 1994–2000. This was a series of artworks the artist made in response to the criminal indifference of the world community in the face of a genocide that claimed one million lives. Jaar travelled to Rwanda in 1994, shortly after the end of the conflict. There he experienced and extensively documented the aftermath of the tragic events, accumulating material that would occupy him for the following six years. Sixteen years later, he returned to Rwanda, having been invited to create a monument to the victims of the genocide. The artist visited hundreds of existing memorials in order to collect the visual materials for his work. The resulting film, exhibited here for the first time, both

provides closure for his work in Rwanda, and expresses continued outrage at the brutal events that could have been prevented.

Jaar asks how we can continue to be emotionally and intellectually affected – to be 'touched' – by events that most of us would prefer not to confront. In a world saturated with media representations of violence and war, how can we stop ourselves becoming de-sensitised? Nothing less than the integrity of humankind is at stake. In the artist's words, 'if images lose their power to affect us, we have lost our humanity'.

Alongside *We Wish to Inform You That We Didn't Know*, Alfredo Jaar also presents *The Marx Lounge* at 52 Renshaw Street.

Frances Loeffler

Film still: *We Wish to Inform You That We Didn't Know* , 2010

Will Kwan
Flame Test, 2010

Mixed media
New commission for Liverpool Biennial 2010, *Touched*

In modern history, the national flag has been the focus of intensely conflicted feelings around national and cultural belonging. The flying of flags at sporting and political events is still the foremost sanctioned symbol of nationalistic pride. Perhaps, however, it's not just the official gestures promoting a nation, but also the unofficial acts of confrontation that more deeply define a country's multivalent identity. Today, both patriotic gestures and acts of political provocation alike have become highly mediated events, endlessly circulated through the channels of the international media and press journalism. How do these gestures affect us and how do they resonate in today's world, when our most raw sensations of belonging or dissent exhibit themselves endlessly for the camera's gaze?

Often involving intensive processes of sociological research, Will Kwan's work brings to the fore the cultural subtexts underlying seemingly neutral everyday objects, systems and devices, such as clocks, maps, flags, language and institutional buildings. Kwan's *Flame Test* is an installation of thirty-six raised flags. Circling the exterior perimeter of a prominent building in Liverpool's city centre, at first sight the flags resemble the colourfully festive decorations of a

national celebration or parade. A closer look, however, reveals each flag to be in flames. In place of nationalist insignia, these banners display photographic documentation of flag-burning incidents taken from the archives of the Associated Press, Reuters, Agence France-Presse and other journalistic agencies. Details from the original scene are just visible in the tightly cropped margins of the prints, serving as a reminder of the multiple frames through which we perceive such highly charged political acts.

The title of the work, *Flame Test*, refers to a testing procedure used in chemistry experiments and indicates the unpredictable character of both political acts and their transmission through media channels. *Flame Test* foregrounds fractured and agonistic evocations of national identity, and reminds us of how the media spectacle reconfigures our most potent symbolic acts of protest, resistance and dissent.

Frances Loeffler

Supported by

Canada Council   Conseil des Arts
for the Arts   du Canada

study for "Touched" 2010 Liverpool Biennial

Study for *Flame Test*, 2010
Courtesy of the artist

... we come closer to understanding
the mimetic character of the
defacement, of the mimetic "fit"
between the object and its defacement

of daring to indicate that obscenity
is built into the quasi-divine
right of authority... M. Taussig

Cristina Lucas

Touch and Go, 2010

16

Single-channel video projection
New commission for Liverpool Biennial 2010, *Touched*

Many people in Liverpool will be familiar with a building on the edge of Chinatown with distinctive rows of windows and the memorable sign across the façade, recalling the company that occupied it: 'Europleasure International Ltd'. This building exemplifies the thriving economy that continued to be expressed through the urban fabric of many western cities until the last two decades of the twentieth century. The companies have long since vanished, but their ghost-like monuments remain. Today, the 'Europleasure building' is an obsolete remnant, a memento of a past economic era. The signage on the façade, with its connotations of materialist excess, is poignantly incongruous against the dilapidation and decay.

Often using humour as a critical strategy, Cristina Lucas's artistic practice overturns the established ideological systems embedded in western society. In *Touch and Go*, a film newly produced for *Touched*, the artist considers the fate of humankind and the built environment as it is caught in the eddies and flows of an unpredictable globalised economy. The video documents a group of unionists and their families throwing stones at the façade of the building. Their act of transgression initially appears as

an unpremeditated and uncontrolled outburst of freedom and anomie, but then reveals a message in broken glass. As the windows shatter – as if blown outwards or violently compressed – the jagged cavities gradually spell out the words 'touch and go'. The expression refers to a momentary act of physical contact, as well as alluding to uncertainty, intermittence and risk. It alludes both to the direct impact and to the transience of large-scale global enterprise. Lucas's work references the imagery of the 1968 riots and rallies in Paris (as in Bertolucci's *The Dreamers*) when workers, students and the bourgeoisie hit the streets in protest together. This blatant act of public vandalism clearly conveys frustration and anger across the social classes, and the fall of political illusion and idealism. The participants emblematically recall the revolutionary spirit of the late 1960s and question its meaning and relevance today.

Lucas's work is a tribute to the force and fragility of a system that has reconfigured our urban environments and then passed on, leaving only remnants in decay. As the artist suggests, we are both affected by and also implicated in the situation; at once vulnerable to its impact, and yet able to inscribe our own marks in the system.

Frances Loeffler

Supported by

Kris Martin
Mandi XV, 2007

Cast bronze, stainless steel
702.2 x 136 cm
Edition of 2 + 1 AP
Courtesy of the artist and Sies + Höke Galerie, Düsseldorf

In myth and legend, swords are symbols of protection, purity and truth. Frequently they have the power of magic attributed to them, and act as harbingers of transformation and the fulfilment of destiny. Kris Martin's deeply contemplative works revolve around the conundrum of existence, its transience, its moments of enchantment and its incomprehensible mysteries.

For *Touched*, the artist presents an up-scaled version of a medieval cruciform sword. Made of bronze and stainless steel, and seven metres in length, this larger-than-life physical realisation of a mythical motif finds a piercing point to cut through and touch our innermost imaginings. The work is part of an ongoing series of works that includes Martin's well-known *Mandi III*, a blank train arrivals and departures board that turns over endlessly without offering either origin or destination. The title, *Mandi*, stems from a colloquial Italian term for 'goodbye', an expression originating from the words *mano* (hand) and *dio* (god) and meaning 'to leave in the hands of God'[1]. *Mandi XV* is here exhibited for the first time as a hanging sword. Suspended in mid-air over our heads, as in the story of Damocles, it is a *memento mori*, posing questions about chance and destiny, and reminding us of the precariousness of all things.

Martin's work offers an allegory of the uncertainty of humankind's journey through life. His work sits squarely within a tradition of conceptual art, yet it engages not only our critical and intellectual faculties, but also deep-felt emotions. In this way, it clearly conjures up the affective dynamic of *Touched*, in which the viewer engages with the artwork equally through the senses, the intellect and the emotions.

Frances Loeffler

1 Jens Hoffman, 'In the hands of God', *Kris Martin*, 2008, Sies + Höke, Düsseldorf, p35.

Supported by

CALOUSTE
GULBENKIAN
FOUNDATION

Detail of the recently restored dome of the Black-E, the site of *Mandi XV*.

Tala Madani

Sunny Side Up, 2010

New commission for Liverpool Biennial 2010, *Touched*

Tala Madani's provocative and exuberant paintings meld the political with the personal to focus on issues of sexual and cultural identity. Men, in particular, are her recurrent subjects. She depicts them with cartoon-like, almost surreal exaggeration, presenting a world as infantile as it is sadistic. Birthday parties, personal grooming sessions and other occasions for male bonding spiral down into bizarre scenarios in which men ritually abuse, humiliate and degrade one another. Luridly colourful, biting in tone and yet always comical in their absurdity, her works have the 'pointed humour and intelligence of political satire, yet are tinged with the bitterness of personal experience'.[1]

Madani's work relates to the themes and concerns of *Touched* in its portrayal of the inadequacies of human, and stereotypically male, relations. She turns a mocking and yet fascinated and empathetic gaze on the cloistered world of male-only get-togethers. Here, 'mankind' is mercilessly (and quite literally) laid bare, in all its embarrassing and perhaps lovable ignobility.

For *Touched*, Madani has produced a new animation, to appear – alongside a group of recent works – at random moments on 'big screens' normally used for broadcasting news and advertisements. This unexpected and sudden encounter with her art aims to highlight the ambivalence of her imagery, at once familiar and disturbing, and to destabilise the expectations of the accidental audience. The friction between form and meaning (a strategy perfectly mastered by the artist) not only questions one's own assumptions and prejudices, but also manages to insinuate a more doubtful and less assertive take on our society. Madani has adopted a similar approach in the preparation of a large outdoor mural that promises to raise a lively debate around the fine line that conventionally separates decorum from vulgarity when it comes to the representation of men and the instrumental use of their body in the public arena. But more importantly, the artist here demonstrates that shame – as a tool of social and political control – can be equally used by and apply to either gender. Her work suggests that it is no longer a weapon for solely establishing and consolidating an indisputable macho/patriarchal leadership.

Frances Loeffler

1 Katherine Holmgren, *frieze*, January 2009

Supported by

Mondriaan Stichting
(Mondriaan Foundation)

Video Still from animation
Accident Series (Taxi Ride), 2009
Courtesy of the artist and Lombard Freid Projects, New York

Raymond Pettibon

Sunday Night and Saturday Morning, 2005

Video animation, DVD, 60 min 45 sec
Edition of 10
Courtesy of the artist and Regen Projects, Los Angeles, California and Sadie Coles HQ, London
Newly commissioned installation including the above animation.

Raymond Pettibon is one of the few visual artists to have achieved almost legendary status in the punk-rock and underground music scene of the American West Coast. Born Raymond Ginn and brother to guitarist/songwriter and impresario Greg Ginn, Pettibon has substantially contributed towards shifting popular genres (such as comics) or formats (fanzine or fly-poster style) from sub-culture to the realm of art.

The first visual reference that comes to mind when approaching Pettibon's art is the comic-book-like work of Roy Lichtenstein. The similarity is only superficial: Pettibon's art is much darker, more cryptic and harder to decipher than Lichtenstein's. Besides, unlike the latter's super-flat mechanised or de-humanised imagery, Pettibon adds gestural strength and anarchic power to the style of comics and introduces a very personal system for cross-referencing quotations, images and his own texts. His codex is much more complex to unpack and less immediate to access.

Arguably, Pettibon's work is like a form of Pop art that has embraced the wild side – punk aesthetics and an angrier social critique. While a distinct political undercurrent is noticeable in his art, to assume that it addresses personal stances would be misleading. As he says: 'It's a mistake to assume about any of my work that it's my own voice. Because that would be the most simple-minded ineffective art that you can make.' Pettibon's work is satirical but he carefully avoids making fun at somebody's expense 'for the sake of a cheap laugh'.[1]

Since the 1990s Raymond Pettibon has challenged and expanded the notion of collage by creating immersive installations that combine works on paper, wall-drawings, prints and other materials. A mixed-media environment, which incorporates the animation entitled *Sunday Night and Saturday Morning* (2005), is his contribution to *Touched*. Pettibon's intervention takes place in one of the most sensitive areas of the city. Located by a cluster of nightlife and music venues, the building that Pettibon temporarily occupies is vacant, dilapidated and sprayed with graffiti and tags. Without erasing these pre-existing traces, in fact by using the same visual strategies and unauthorised street style, the artist attempts both to bring this site to life and life to art.

Lorenzo Fusi

1 Both quotations are from an interview with the artist which can be found at www.pbs.org/art21/artists/pettibon/clip2.html

Supported by

The Henry Moore
Foundation

© Raymond Pettibon

Do Ho Suh
Bridging Home, 2010

11

Mixed media outdoor installation
New commission for Liverpool Biennial 2010, *Touched*

Do Ho Suh came to the attention of the international art world in 2001 when he represented Korea at the 49th Venice Biennale. His life and art are split between two realms, Korea being his home country and America his adoptive one, and his practice continuously attempts to bridge these two cultural spheres or biographical references.

His interest in collective and personal space derives from his Korean upbringing. As the artist remarks, Seoul is a very crowded city. Because of this population density, it is completely acceptable for a person to invade the private space of another, and the perception of individual space is significantly different from elsewhere. In Do Ho Suh's case, the sense of unavoidable physical proximity that one typically experiences in any Asian metropolis was augmented by his undertaking two years' compulsory military service. The army transformed the artist's own body into a plural entity, following the basic military principle of cohabitation informed by the paradigm of togetherness, in consequence of which the Self is depersonalised in favour of the collective Us. Works such as *Uni-Form/s: Self Portrait/s: My 39 Years* (2006) – a rack displaying all the uniforms worn by the artist throughout his life both at school

and in the army – clearly address Do Ho Suh's concerns about the impact of the homogeneity enforced by uniforms on the personality and freedom of individuals.

Memory plays a key role in the artist's work, as does nostalgia, most noticeably in his ethereal reconstructions of Korean buildings, transparent and evanescent as in a dream, suspended in a sort of timeless limbo. The artist, notwithstanding his longing for the past, is aware that nothing remains the same. His memories (although meticulously translated in his works) never match the actual state of things.

More recently, Do Ho Suh has explored the possibility of coming to terms with his divided cultural background through syncretic elements that integrate eastern and western influences. Moving against the notion of cultural clash (that is to say two worlds or civilisations colliding), he is currently envisioning a new cultural and visual domain, which results from the fusion of his diverse and, at times, conflicting experiences. The seeds of the artist's process of hybridisation now fertilise the British soil with this new commission for *Touched*.

Lorenzo Fusi

Supported by

The Henry Moore
Foundation

Preparatory sketch for *Bridging Home*, 2010
Image courtesy the artist

Héctor Zamora
Synclastic/Anticlastic, 2010

12

50 mm cast concrete shell structures (series of 7 variations/moulds)
200 pieces produced
Courtesy of the artist
New commission for Liverpool Biennial 2010, *Touched*

Working across a variety of media, Héctor Zamora intervenes in the social and physical structures of urban spaces. His works draw on extensive research into specific socio-political topographies, while also playing on the inhabitants' collective memories, myths and desires. For the Venice Biennale, 2009, he created a fleet of dirigibles, both real and imaginary. These settled, inexplicably, over the rooftops one morning, and lodged in the narrow side-streets of the city.

Reflecting on one of Colombia's primary export industries, in Bogotá the artist filled an entire storey of a vacant building with a multitude of bananas, so many that they burst from the open windows. Zamora's exaggerated gesture caused passers-by going about their day-to-day business to pause momentarily as they looked up at this strange reappropriation of space performed by nature. The processes of transformation and decay that the fruit underwent through the length of the exhibition period ensured that the patches of colour filling the empty windows were always changing in shade and tonality: as a living organism, the façade of this disused building adjusted daily to the passage of time.

Héctor Zamora reinterprets the status quo – the socio-political and built environment we live in – by envisaging situations and scenarios that induce us to take a different viewpoint. In so doing, he 'touches' our everyday experiences, pulling us momentarily out of the mundane and quotidian, and shifting our understanding of the world around us, so that we can see it anew. Although rigorous in his analysis of the context, and almost scientific in the development of his projects, Zamora nevertheless humanises the cityscape in which he operates by exposing the links that bind the constructed and the living elements of the city. His interventions often occupy marginal interstices or unnoticeable sites, which he transforms into creatures and organisms able to verbalise the city's intimate contradictions.

Irony and a sense of humour are also key elements in his art. Zamora's playfulness compensates for the seriousness of his interventions, just as his organic approach to architecture and urban planning ensures that his work is never overbearing but suggestive, sympathetic and insightful.

Lorenzo Fusi

Project Sponsor

Supported by

The Henry Moore Foundation

neptune

Photo courtesy of the artist

Tate Liverpool

Albert Dock, L3 4BB
Open: Tuesday–Sunday 10.00–17.50
Closed Mondays (except Bank Holiday Mondays)
Tel: +44 (0) 151 702 7400   www.tate.org.uk/liverpool
Free Entry   Fully Accessible

'Touched' suggests not just the idea of being emotionally affected, but also an immediate sense of proximity, action and physical contact – aspects you would not necessarily expect to encounter in a museum or art gallery. For decades, however, international artists have questioned the idea that visual art should be static, sanctified and presented on a wall or plinth to be viewed from a distance. Most notably, the idea that the work of art is imbued with an untouchable aura to be protected from physical and emotional engagement was questioned through the emergence of challenging and sometimes rebellious artistic strategies in the 1960s. *Touched* at Tate Liverpool refers to this period in art history to explore the ways in which contemporary artists continue to respond to and build upon these ideas today.

Magdalena Abakanowicz, Otto Muehl and Franz West, artists who are presented here, came to prominence in the 1960/70s and pioneered practices that explored the ways in which life could be unified with our experience of art. These figures are brought together with a younger generation of artists to reflect on the theme of *Touched* through a range of multifaceted manifestations. Conceived as a 'sculptural happening', the exhibition features on-going live interventions and appearances by artists, performing objects, as well as installations and sculptures to be probed and explored by the audience within the gallery.

While the new commissions for the *Touched* exhibition share the spirit of being 'touched', they are equally concerned with challenging and subverting the physicality and torpor of the object. More importantly the artworks in the exhibition explore the relationship between the tangible and the intangible, as reflected through the coexistence of absence and presence (Jamie Isenstein); enclosure and exposure (Wannes Goetschalckx); structure and its disintegration (Eva Kot'átková); the physical and the metaphorical (Nina Canell); and through proximity and distance (Alfredo and Isabel Aquilizan, and Diango Hernández). Tate Liverpool's contribution to *Touched* looks at poetic, subversive, intimate and up-front moments where these opponents touch each other in the realm of the arts.

Peter Gorschlüter

Tate Liverpool
Gallery floor plans

Ground Floor

Magdalena
Abakanowicz

Lifts

Entrance

Fourth Floor

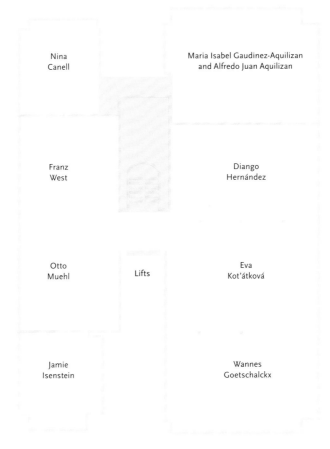

Nina
Canell

Maria Isabel Gaudinez-Aquilizan
and Alfredo Juan Aquilizan

Franz
West

Diango
Hernández

Otto
Muehl

Lifts

Eva
Kot'átková

Jamie
Isenstein

Wannes
Goetschalckx

Magdalena Abakanowicz
Embryology, 1978–80

13

Mixed media
Dimensions variable
Tate collection

Magdalena Abakanowicz is one of the most revered Polish sculptors living today. Since the early-1960s her practice has been primarily concerned with organic form and the use of textiles as a sculptural medium. A recurring element throughout her work is the human body which provides a source of creative and imaginative inspiration. Abakanowicz has deployed a range of sculptural processes in her work, from taking casts of bodily forms in the *Backs* series (1976–1980) to weaving soft objects using threads pulled from discarded ropes in the *Abakans*, a celebrated cycle of large-scale three-dimensional textile works. Among her most famous and striking works is *Embryology* (1978–80), which has recently been acquired by the Tate Collection. This sculptural installation comprises hundreds of hand-sewn objects of varying sizes that are loosely stacked and scattered around the gallery to create an environment that evokes the natural landscape. Abakanowicz's installation confronts us with an ambigious and disturbing place between bodies and amorphous organic matter, while the title and form of the work suggest cocooned life-forms about to emerge and flourish. The textile sack-like skin and spilled interior stuffing also suggest ideas of

trade and storage, particularly in the context of Tate Liverpool which is housed in a converted warehouse.

First presented at the Venice Biennial in 1980, *Embryology* is now being shown for the first time in the UK. It offers a succinct correspondence with the theme of the Biennial, and constitutes the opening element of *Touched* at Tate Liverpool. Abakanowicz's practice continues to resonate with younger generations of artists and the inclusion of *Embryology* within the Biennial provides an historical backdrop against which to view and experience the exhibition's newly commissioned works. Premiering the display of the work as part of *Touched* also positions the Tate Collection and its remit to acquire works of art from across the globe in relation to the theme of 'touched'.

Peter Gorschlüter

POLSKA! YEAR is a cultural programme coordinated by the Adam Mickiewicz Institute in Warsaw, comprising over 200 projects that present the most interesting achievements of Polish culture to the British public in the fields of visual arts, theatre, music, film and literature. www.polskayear.pl

Supported by

Venice Biennial, Polish Pavillon, 1980
Photo: A. Starewicz

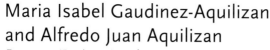

Maria Isabel Gaudinez-Aquilizan and Alfredo Juan Aquilizan

13

Passage (Project Another Country), 2010

Mixed media installation with participatory elements
New commission for Tate Liverpool and Liverpool Biennial 2010, *Touched*

The work of Filipino artists Isabel and Alfredo Aquilizan addresses individuals and their personal stories, histories and belongings, as well as their creativity and dreams. Their practice is collaborative in method, making use of the accumulation and rearrangement of physical objects and narratives. Often existing communities and an institutional 'public' are invited to engage together in the production of the artwork. In this way, the artists create communal experiences initiated by collecting domestic items, such as blankets, clothing and toiletries, displaced and transformed by meticulous reorganisation. In this way, their projects build, accumulate and dissect collective memories – and hopes for the future.

For their *Touched* commission, Isabel and Alfredo Aquilizan have explored what is specific to a particular place and the inter-connectivity of experiences between peoples and communities around the world. As a departure point, they considered how the life and history of people in Australia – where they have been based since 2006 – relates to the realities and experiences of people in Liverpool. How might the sea – as a

physical and metaphorical threshold on whichever side of the globe – inform our thinking and longing for a different and better life? How and to where do we project our dreams and longings?

In the run-up to *Touched*, and partly continuing throughout, communities and families in Liverpool have been building small boats out of recycled 'removals' boxes, contributing their own communities of boat-shelters to the gallery installation. Presented together, the objects connote real or imagined journeys; they offer a reflection on forced or voluntary migration, as well as a meditation on the impossibility of escaping our own identity and place of origin.

Peter Gorschlüter

Courtesy of the artists

This project has been assisted by the Australian Government through the Australia Council for the Arts, its arts funding and advisory body.

Nina Canell

Perpetuum Mobile (40 kg), 2009–2010

Mixed media, dimensions variable
Courtesy Konrad Fischer Galerie, Mother's Tankstation & Galerie Barbara Wien
New commission for Tate Liverpool and Liverpool Biennial 2010, *Touched*

13

The work of Swedish artist Nina Canell explores the relationship between humans, objects and events, whereby the parameters of material phenomena might be articulated. Her installations are carefully choreographed to create seemingly casual sculptural happenings, which harness the properties and elusive energies inherent, for instance, in sound, gas and water – revealing intimate bonds in our existing as well as fictive surroundings. Incremental shifts in frequency, radiation and movement are often exposed in the contingent 'nothingness' between us and that which we perceive, thus suggesting alternative readings of what might be regarded as invisible or imperceptible.

For *Touched*, Canell uses water, a recurring element in her work which also references Liverpool's position as a seaport. Taking its cue from the last musical passage in Gustav Holst's composition '*Neptune the Mystic*' from his *Planets* suite (in which Holst conceived of what is often described as the first 'fade-out' in music), Canell presents a perfectly static object in which she has recorded an imaginative descending movement by capturing the fluctuating depths of the River Mersey

with an oceanographic 'Nansen Bottle'. The act of waning or giving way – to grow duller and dimmer until something is completely washed out – thus leaps from the pages of a musical score and plunges into a quiet underwater event. In some ways the transparency of the water defies visible distinction, thus allowing the precisely measured action to open the mind's eye in attempt to define the logic of its strata. Such skewing of the senses into the prose-like realm is a typical gesture in Canell's work, which often seeks to address a personal position to physical phenomena.

A community of objects and happenings accompanies the work, which further explores the link between the gallery space and the outside world in a second marine endeavour. This work relies on chance transmissions from a buoy on the River Mersey, which records the acoustic topography of the water with a hydrophone, to a radio receiver in the gallery space. Thus, radio and water waves establish a symbiotic coexistence, establishing yet another alternating point in Canell's fluctuating geometry.

Peter Gorschlüter

Supported by

CALOUSTE
GULBENKIAN
FOUNDATION

EMBASSY OF SWEDEN

Wannes Goetschalckx
1 WITHOUT

Video and mixed media
New commission for Tate Liverpool and Liverpool Biennial 2010, *Touched*

Belgian artist Wannes Goetschalckx explores the emotional and physical, and the ideological and imaginative, in relation to the body and space. His practice combines videos, objects and performance actions in sculptural settings that are occupied, probed and altered by Goetschalckx's own intervention. By posing physical and mental challenges to his own mind and body, his work aims to reveal to the viewer both the immediately apparent and also the hidden and psychic constraints that bear on human life. The coexistence of comfort and pain, exposure and enclosure, and cage and shelter are frequent denominators in his practice.

For *Touched*, Goetschalckx has developed a multi-channel video installation comprising short films depicting the artist engaged in everyday actions and rituals within a minimal wooden space. Performed in hermetic solitude, Goetschalckx's actions reflect upon the behavioural possibilities and rituals that might be enacted by a single human being or creature 'in captivity'. The setting of the videos reappears in modified form within the gallery as a space for activity

and contemplation where visitors can experience a 'warm' shelter, acting as a counterpoint to the 'cold' white cube presentation of the video installation. The title of the work, 1 WITHOUT, alludes to the composite of words and meanings within Goetschalckx's spoken language – in Dutch 'wit' means 'white' and 'hout' means 'wood' – while also referencing the 'empty' twelfth plinth that forms part of the installation and that becomes an occasional platform for live interventions by the artist.

Peter Gorschlüter

Supported by

CALOUSTE
GULBENKIAN
FOUNDATION

Diango Hernández
Homesick, 2010

Courtesy of Alexander and Bonin, NY and Michael Wiesehöfer, Cologne
New commission for Tate Liverpool and Liverpool Biennial 2010, *Touched*

13

Productive in a diversity of media, including sculpture, installation, music and drawing, the practice of Diango Hernández is grounded in the desire to capture ephemeral moments of beauty, seduction and conviction. The artist grew up and studied in Havana before moving to Europe, and his work is inspired by his recollection of Cuba's political and economic crisis in the wake of the collapse of the socialist systems in Eastern Europe. Following these events, his work began to subtly comment on circumstances, places and opinions related to political ideologies, propaganda and utopian beliefs. In counterpoint to this, life in Havana, with 'the unbelievable blend of races, smells, styles, sounds and fears' experienced by Hernández, continues to inform and resonate throughout his artistic practice.

Hernández once stated that 'the first chair we have ever touched may contain all the possible happiness in the universe'. In his works Hernández explores ideas of the quotidian, and everyday objects are imbued with symbolic value and transformative potential. His new multi-part commission for *Touched* focuses on the notion of 'home' and the sickness we experience in its absence. In the gallery the audience encounters physical structures and patterns made out of dispersed and deconstructed furniture elements, solitary objects rotating on stages as if touched by a ghostly hand, theatre curtains and a suspended stairway, all of which apparently connect in a dreamlike and surreal setting. As opposed to a mere mimetic representation, Hernández's work constitutes an exploration into the psyche of what we regard as home. He invites the viewer to travel to an imaginative realm to discover a miraculous scene that is informed and heightened by memory and personal history.

The installation is accompanied by a new series of small collages entitled *My postcards never get home...*, presented as postcard fragments mounted on photosensitive paper whose colour changes in response to light levels within the space. Ultimately, Diango Hernández's work explores ideas of memory and changeability to reflect on the unavailing longing to retain a sense of permanence and stability.

Peter Gorschlüter

Supported by

i f a ∎ Institut für Auslandsbeziehungen e. V.

My postcards never get home..., 2010
Mixed media

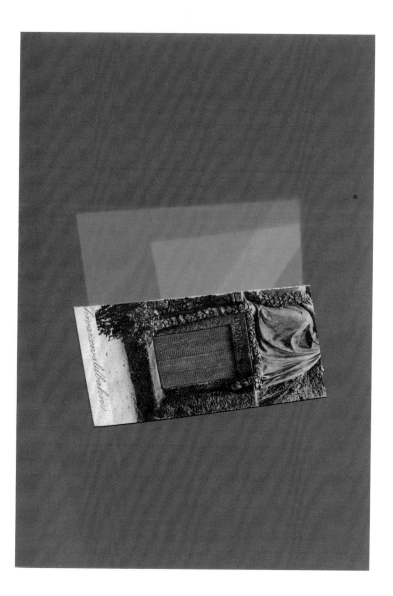

Jamie Isenstein
Empire of Fire, 2010

Mixed media
New commission for Tate Liverpool and Liverpool Biennial 2010, *Touched*

The artworks of New York-based Jamie Isenstein confront the visitor with the unexpected and inexplicable. Isenstein explores the interplay of performance and sculpture, contesting the status of sculpture as an inanimate object. By inhabiting the artworks with her own body, Isenstein combines sculptural practice and 'endurance performance art' with elements of absurdist humour. In many of her objects and theatrical installations, the artist is contained within the object itself, her body never fully revealed. Even when Isenstein is not performing the piece, a temporary sign stating 'will return' or 'gone fishing' is displayed to ensure that the artwork continues. Drawing inspiration from Surrealism, in particular the paintings of René Magritte and the writings of Georges Bataille, Isenstein's work explores the idea of the uncanny, and notions of revelation and concealment, presence and absence.

For *Touched*, Isenstein is presenting a new work that involves the artist's presence over the entire duration of the exhibition. In the centre of the gallery sits a large cluster of stuff: furniture such as tables, a chair and a fireplace, and things from everyday life – among other decorative objects, a bronze sculpture and a pile of books – have been haphazardly pushed to the centre of the room. The setting alludes to the stacked interior of what might have been a drawing room in Second Empire style, or the stage props of a theatre set for the Sartre play *No Exit*. As if by a miracle the objects are on fire, with little flames emerging from them, yet they do not burn. As almost self-sufficient monuments that commemorate their own existence, they call attention to their permanence and invoke a notion of eternity. From the corner of the gallery, witnessing the mysterious gathering of objects on fire, is what at first appears to be a standard-issue fire hose... Beware! In Jamie Isenstein's work nothing is as it seems.

Peter Gorschlüter

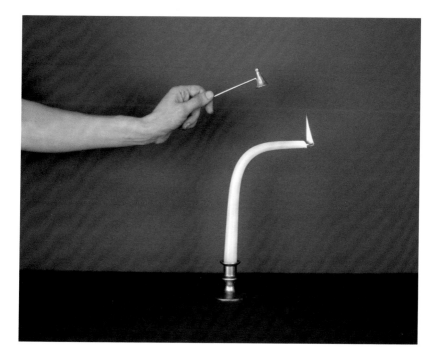

Eva Kot'átková
Stories from the Living Room, 2010

13

Mixed media
New commission for Tate Liverpool and Liverpool Biennial 2010, *Touched*

The Czech artist Eva Kot'átková investigates personal space, everyday actions and situations, and the relationship between people and their surroundings. Through live interventions in given spaces, and sculptural constructions probed by the artist or willing participants, Kot'átková examines common contemporary gestures and rituals. She is particularly interested in how we are affected by the experiences of childhood, especially educational institutions, with their rules, policies and physical restrictions. Kot'átková uses personal observation and encounters with her participants to develop alternative, and at times surreal, devices and related actions that simultaneously question and propose human relationships within specifically defined frameworks.

Kot'átková's project for *Touched* brings together people from Liverpool at different stages of life whose experiences and personal histories have been informed by a variety of social environments. Over several weeks some school children and some adults met separately and together in order to share

and record – with various devices and in different formats – their respective life stories. Facilitated by the artist and Tate Learning curators, the children became the initiators of the discussions, interviewing the adults and deploying alternative methods of reconstructing, evaluating and archiving personal histories. During the second stage of the project children became the mediators of the adults' life stories, being filmed reinterpreting and retelling in the first person the stories and memories of the adults.

During the exhibition the project continues to evolve, revealing in the gallery as a social structure comprising elements of an archive, functioning as a place for encounter between participants and 'public', and providing a stage for multi-faceted events and activities inspired by the conversations.

Peter Gorschlüter

Supported by

CALOUSTE GULBENKIAN FOUNDATION

CZECH CENTRE
ČESKÉ CENTRUM
www.czechcentre.org.uk

old person
carried on legs
of children

Otto Muehl
Selected Works 2004–2010

Now living in Portugal, the Austrian Otto Muehl (b. 1925) is one of the most radical artists of the twentieth century. In the 1960s, with Hermann Nitsch, Günter Brus and Rudolf Schwarzkogler, he co-founded the Viennese Actionist Group. Their practice was characterised by the expressive and performative use of the body, objectified and subjected to ritualistic methods of extreme physical abuse, often with sexual connotations. Muehl's work later shifted from direct confrontation with sexual taboos towards an analysis of behaviour and action as a foundation for the achievement of an alternative society. In the 1970s he initiated *Aktions-Analytische Organisation*, a community of people concerned with the utopian unification of art and life outside mainstream society.

Explicitly provocative and politically charged in nature, many of Muehl's early actions can also be regarded as expanding the language of painting through the expressive use of various fluids such as paint, bodily liquids and food in relation to the body. But throughout his career, traditional painterly practice has played a critical role as a means of expressing human obsession and rejecting bourgeois ideology.

For *Touched*, Muehl presents a series of recent paintings using acid colours applied in expressive gestures (so harking back to the techniques used in his early action painting). The paintings are populated by a cartoon-like set of characters, for instance *Untitled* (2007), which confronts the viewer with a stark female figure. In other works, animals – most notably the shark – are used to relate allegorically to a world obsessed with money. The shark assumes multiple meanings, ranging from a symbol of fear to a representation of total freedom from social restraint. The simple and expressive power of these late works exemplifies Muehl's lifelong preoccupation with painting, while also demonstrating aspects of chance and physical action.

Peter Gorschlüter

Supported by

austrian cultural forumlon

Also showing

Arche Otto, 2010
Acrylic on canvas,
140 x 140 cm

Conversation, 2007
Acrylic on canvas, 70 x 70 cm

Untitled, 2004
Acrylic on canvas, 70 x 50 cm

Untitled, 2005
Oil on canvas, 120 x 120 cm

Untitled, 2007
Acrylic on canvas,
80 x 100 cm

Untitled, 2007
Acrylic on canvas, 70 x 80 cm

Untitled, 2007
Acrylic on canvas, 80 x 70 cm

Untitled, 2008
Acrylic on canvas

Franz West

Smears, 2010

13

Aluminum lacquered
New commission for Tate Liverpool and Liverpool Biennial 2010, *Touched*

Viennese artist Franz West (b. 1947) is one of the most renowned sculptors living today. Throughout his career he has questioned the notion of art as an object for mere passive contemplation. Whilst exploring various ways of allowing the audience to interact and engage with his art, he has deliberately stressed the materiality of his work by using media including plaster, papier-mâché, wire, polyester and aluminium to create sculpture and installation works that probe the boundary between organic and geometric form.

Being influenced by the extremely physical and confrontational work of the Viennese Actionists, in particular the performance-based work of Otto Muehl, West gained attention in the early 1980s for his *Adaptives*, a series of small-scale portable sculptures designed as playthings to be handled. These works helped expand the concept of sculpture towards an encouragement of physical interchange and performative experience, paving the way for a reconsideration of sculptural practice in the second half of the twentieth century. Since the late 1980s

West's work has evolved to explore the realms of interior design, furniture and display, and his sculpture has grown in scale, inhabiting a variety of spaces within many of the world's most respected museums, as well as large-scale public realm projects.

Exploring the relationship between the quotidian and the exceptional, the functional and the abstract, and in response to the theme of *Touched*, West has produced a new large-scale sculpture entitled *Smears*. In the tradition of his previous works, he intends it to be 'a sculpture that can not only be viewed from a distance but experienced whilst sitting on, lying on and touching it'. The form resembles a gigantic impasto loop of paint that seems to have escaped from the artist's studio and is presented as an oversized object 'applied' to Tate Liverpool's galleries. The audience is invited to interact with the work in the space.

Peter Gorschlüter

Photo: Galerie Meyer Kainer, Vienna

Supported by

CALOUSTE
GULBENKIAN
FOUNDATION

The Henry Moore
Foundation

austrian⁺cultural forum^lon

the Bluecoat

School Lane, L1 3BX
Open: daily 10.00–18.00
Tel: +44 (0) 151 702 5324   www.thebluecoat.org.uk
Free Entry   Fully Accessible

Touched provoked us to ask questions such as how are humans touched by seeing or making art? How or why does a moving experience stay with you? How can an artist's work be inspired through an understanding of what touches people?

The work of the four invited artists suggests possible responses. They employ strategies that revolve around the trace of memory and matter, identity and humour, and they often use familiar objects in unusual or unexpected ways. The kinship in their work suggests a glimpse of everyday situations from very different worlds. The global and the local collide, collapse and fuse through explorations of YouTube viral wit, urban regeneration and architecture, identity and personal politics.

Several of the commissioned works show the hand of the maker in a very direct way, presenting tactile qualities that highlight an intense (some might say obsessive) engagement with materials and the body. In this respect the works embody aspects of a debate about different ways of creating meaning in art: how does value and meaning become attached to the material and formal presence of objects more readily associated with traditions in craft? Do these differ from values and meaning ascribed to work conventionally defined as fine art? Is there an argument that the former is necessarily more 'touched' than the latter?

Sara-Jayne Parsons

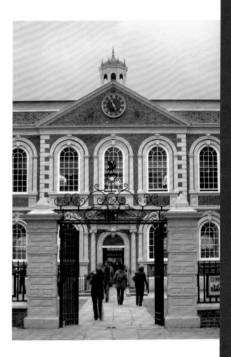

the Bluecoat
Gallery floor plans

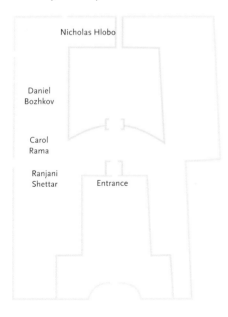

Nicholas Hlobo

Daniel
Bozhkov

Carol
Rama

Ranjani
Shettar

Entrance

Daniel Bozkov
Music Not Good For Pigeons, 2010

10

Benches, massage table, football players' shirts, music - video projection,
YouTube video, monitors, soft toys
Commissioned by the Bluecoat and Liverpool Biennial 2010 for *Touched*

Daniel Bozkov often characterises his site-specific works as 'situation retrievals'. Created after months of research and engagement with a particular location, his projects draw attention to unusual coincidences and reveal hidden strains of meaning. To unearth instances of surprising proximity he spends a great deal of time with a variety of people, learning first-hand about their personal history, experiences and practice, and sharing his own stories and expertise in exchange for new skills. Bozkov's work acquires its form in a process of social anthropology. Appropriate means are decided along the way – painting, photography, film or interventions on the city street. He has even developed a new *eau de cologne* and a type of bread as ways to engage with specific situations and sites.

For *Touched* Bozkov examined his memories of the Liverpool he first visited in 1986 as a sailor when he knew it as the home of the Beatles, an historic trading port and a place where local left-wing politicians had stood up to the policies of Margaret Thatcher. Bozkov clearly remembers seeing his first homeless person on that brief seven-hour visit, a memory confusingly muddled with Bulgarian Communist propaganda that

taught him that homelessness was a social plague of the West.

On his second visit nearly 25 years later, Bozkov investigates the discrepancies between what caught his attention then and now. Merging the phenomenon of online culture with football, music and politics, his reflection is darkly humorous, poignant and timely. The main structure of Bozkov's installation is a replica of the dressing rooms of Liverpool Football Club. When he visited the Anfield stadium, the artist was struck by how humble and austere these spaces were. At the centre of the structure at the centre of the structure a YouTube video of a sneezing panda cub, viewed by over 60 million people world-wide, plays repeatedly on several monitors. A music video that presents the half-forgotten, but still controversial, history of Militant Tendency – a Trotskyist group within the British Labour Party, which played a crucial role in Liverpool City Council's struggle against the Conservative government of Margaret Thatcher between 1983 and 1987.

Bozkov interviewed several of these former Militant Tendency councillors, and then painted a series of frescoes inside the cells of the recently closed Somerset County Jail in Skowhegan,

Courtesy of the artist

Supported by

CALOUSTE
GULBENKIAN
FOUNDATION

Maine, recounting chapters of Militant's story. These frescoes appear in a music video along with Bozhkov taking voice lessons in Liverpool, learning how to sing John Lennon's 'Imagine'. Performed in collaboration with local musicians and bands, in a style changing from bluegrass to punk to Socialist and anti-Fascist songs, Bozhkov provocatively suggests that the message Lennon embedded in the song could be viewed through a more specific local political lens.

Sara-Jayne Parsons

Nicholas Hlobo

Ndize, 2010

Recycled rubber, fabric, ribbon, white clay
Commissioned by the Bluecoat and Liverpool Biennial 2010 for *Touched*

Nicholas Hlobo creates sculptural installations that explore and reflect his Xhosa heritage. Personal and collective memory slides in and out of focus as he reframes and re-presents traditions and rites of passage. With intelligence and sensitivity, Hlobo considers how such customs are evolving in changing times. Entwined with this cultural scrutiny, the artist engages in an investigation of sexual identity and personal politics, contemplating his position as a gay man within Xhosa culture in post-apartheid South Africa.

In his investigation of past and present Hlobo reinvents and recycles objects. His materials often include leather, rubber, ribbon, furniture and other domestic found objects. The obsessive stitching, braiding and knotting he frequently employs reveals an intensity of making that revolves around craft and touch. The tactile nature of his materials and his hand-worked methods imply tradition and skill, but result in something that is more contemporary than historical in meaning. Unsurprisingly, Hlobo sometimes performs with his sculptures, partly dressed as – or in – one of his forms, further highlighting the significant relationship of materials and body.

For *Touched* Hlobo connects two galleries with a trail of rubber, fabric and white clay balls, enticing visitors into a game of hide-and-seek with his sculptural installation *Ndize*. In Xhosa the game of hide-and-seek is called 'undize', and 'ndize' is the player who seeks. Hlobo introduces us to 'ndize' in the ground-floor gallery; a lone figure leaning against the window, peering out, suggestively presenting his rear and silently counting before the search begins. From 'ndize' the playful trail winds its way around and out of the gallery, meandering up the stairs, in search of the other players.

Once upstairs, visitors are met with a sensuous maze of brightly coloured, densely woven ribbons that hang from a great height to the floor. For seekers in the game there are several paths to choose from; the labyrinth is delicious in its intimacy and mystery. Brief, tantalising glimpses through the ribbons reveal the hiding players, and after the challenge of wrong turns and dead ends, seekers may eventually find them; an enigmatic couple engaged in a whispered conversation. It is not clear what sex they are. Their black rubber bodies are clothed with fabric and yet more rubber; their hands and faces are doll-like. Upon finding the hiding players the innocence of the game of hide-and-seek matures into the caress of adult fantasy.

Sara-Jayne Parsons

Carol Rama
The Cabinet of Carol Rama

Carol Rama is a self-taught artist who has been making art for nearly seventy years. Producing work consistently characterised as unconventional and darkly erotic, Rama's style has moved from figurative to abstract and back again through the decades, accompanied by an exploration of diverse materials. Throughout, her work has had a constant subject: an engagement with self and the effect of trauma in modern life.

Rama began making art to express her fears and anguish; emotions of passion, anger, violence, joy and melancholy are all strongly conveyed in the work. Yet the artist has also indicated that she has used art to heal herself from despair and loneliness, drawing strongly on personal experiences of devastating loss from her mother's mental illness to the trauma of her father's suicide. This makes for uneasy reading, her work avoiding narrative in favour of symbolism, provocation and enchantment. Its power lies in dichotomy: there is something fierce and tender about her female figures; they are seductive but repulsive, tragic yet playful.

Featuring twelve works (ten of which have never been seen in the UK before),

The Cabinet of Carol Rama includes dresses made and worn by the artist, along with watercolours, collages, sculpture and photographs. The selection, spanning a sixty-year period, effectively creates a very intimate space; a place referencing not only clothing, the female body and the hint of sexual encounters, but, more significantly, Rama's biography and the private realm of her own home and studio.

Watercolours from the late 1930s featuring impassioned sexualised young women converse with images of more opaque indicators of desire such as stylish shoes with phallic details, fox stoles and a crowd of luscious shaving brushes. Collectively the motifs present themes of sexual identity with a specific investigation of female sensuality. Later works, collages on canvas from the 1960s and 1970s, explore the soft, skin-like surface of rubber inner tubes. These anticipate her more direct focus on the body in the following decade – Rama's series of black wedding dresses featuring hand-stitched details echoing the forms of male and female genitalia.

Sara-Jayne Parsons

With thanks to Alexandra Wetzel and Franco Masoero

Ranjani Shettar
Aureole, 2010

Cast bronze
Dimensions variable
Courtesy of the artist and Talwar Gallery, New York and Delhi

The relationship that humans have to particular spaces in the built environment is a consistent concern for Ranjani Shettar. She is interested in the scrape or collision between the industrial and the organic, the mundane and the unusual, the traditional and the contemporary. She searches for possibilities of meaning in humble objects and usually works with everyday materials such as wax, ink, paper, cotton, plastic sheeting or mud.

For *Touched*, Shettar has experimented with bronze and presents an elegant installation in the Vide at the Bluecoat that provokes a conversation about the touch between materials and architecture. Cast using the ancient lost wax process, Shettar's work draws attention to the process of casting bronze. Traditionally, small 'sprue', or channels, are used to facilitate the flow of molten bronze and allow ventilation from the main form being cast. These channels typically appear as vein-like structures but are cut off the main form and discarded in the finishing process; their existence is purely functional.

Aureole embraces the idea of these 'lost' forms and recreates them as a large, closed organic form that slopes away from the viewer, circling, ascending and clinging to the walls and floor of the Vide. Made of several pieces varying in length from just a few inches to several feet, the bronze resembles the remnants of a collapsed spider web.

A poetic tension and mystery permeates the installation; a sense that something cast has been removed, leaving only the trace of what it once was; a voluminous ghost that hovers unseen. Similarly, the vine-like natural growth of the roughened bronze with green patina sits in stark contrast to the grey-white, smooth, geometric minimalism of the surrounding architecture.

In creating *Aureole* Shettar made the wax models for the work and then supervised the production of the bronze by a team of craftsmen at a foundry in south-eastern India, an area renowned since the ninth century for producing Chola bronzes.[1] She not only challenged her practice by deciding to work with bronze, but also questioned the role of the maker's hand; although using a traditional craft method, she employed a different form not usually associated with the method or material. Significantly the young men helping her see themselves as fabricators; they are not self-aware as artists or craftsmen. In this respect, it's clear that Shettar's work continues to occupy a liminal creative space; a place where the thresholds between art and craft, tradition and modernity overlap and inform each other.

Sara-Jayne Parsons

1   Chola-style bronze is epitomised by statues of Hindu gods and other ceremonial deities usually made to be housed in an inner sanctum of a temple, and being brought out only for certain rituals or festivals. By and large they are very expressive and technically exquisite.

Open Eye Gallery

28–32 Wood Street, L1 4AQ
Open: Tuesday–Sunday 10.30–17.30
Tel: +44 (0) 151 709 7460   www.openeye.org.uk
Free Entry   Fully Accessible (the gallery is above street level
but there is an external lift for access)

For *Touched*, Open Eye Gallery has chosen to work with just one artist: Lars Laumann. Laumann makes video essays that are driven by his fascination with people and their complex interior worlds – he points up their strangeness, separateness and need to connect. He explores collisions of individuals, cultures, ways of life and systems of belief. Combining elements of documentary with fiction, poetry and myth, he creates extraordinary stories that plunge us into the lives of his subjects.

Berlinmuren (2008) tells the story of Eija-Riitta Eklöf Berliner-Mauer, a Swedish woman who describes herself as 'objectum sexual'. She believes that all objects have souls and feelings – she is married to the Berlin Wall and has converted her house into a 'Museum of Guillotines and Models'. The film's collage of found materials and live action is underpinned by the precise, intense voice of its subject. It imbues alien ideas and absurd events – such as the bizarre final scenes of David Hasselhoff performing on the Berlin Wall in 1989 – with seriousness and pathos.

Laumann's 2009 video *Shut up child, this ain't bingo* revolves around his close friend Kjersti Andvig and her relationship with death-row prisoner Carlton Turner. To be closer to Turner, Andvig moves to Texas, where she is drawn into the religion-suffused world of her landlady. By the time of Turner's execution, Andvig earnestly believes that he will be raised from the dead and returned to them. She touches him for the first time a few minutes after his execution.

Driven by obsession, love and longing, Laumann's subjects are on the margins of our idea of what is 'normal'. They are not, however, offered up as exotic objects of pity or fear, nor are they fixed in an affectless, Warholian gaze. He may be led by curiosity, but his engagement is sincere and sustained. He dares to look, and he dares us to look with him, exposing the hypocrisy of the politely averted gaze, levelling the ground between viewer and viewed.

Patrick Henry

Lars Laumann

8

Helen Keller (and the great purging bonfire of books and unpublished manuscripts illuminating the dark), 2010

Video for projection
New commission for Liverpool Biennial 2010, *Touched*

Morrissey Foretelling the Death of Diana, 2006

Video for projection
Courtesy Maureen Paley, London

Duett (Med styrken i vår tro i en sang, i en sang), 2010

Video for large screen (loop)
Courtesy Maureen Paley, London

For *Touched*, Open Eye Gallery has commissioned Lars Laumann to create a new work, which is exhibited alongside two existing works. The commissioned work, *Helen Keller (and the great purging bonfire of books and unpublished manuscripts illuminating the dark)*, is a video essay in two parts. It uses a range of techniques and approaches to discuss filmic and literary adaptation, multiple narratives, censorship and the burning of books. The first part, 'Kari & Knut', is based on the texts of Helen Keller. Born in Alabama in 1880, Keller was an author, lecturer and political activist; she was blind and deaf – she lived in complete darkness and silence. The video uses found footage from an Iranian adaptation of J. D. Salinger's 1963 novelette *Franny and Zooey* to tell the story of Helen Keller's banned books, *The Frost King* and *How I Became a Socialist*. The second part ('Sweden – Antichrist's Miracle?') is a collage of found and produced elements. They revolve around a 1960s adaptation of the Swedish author Selma Lagerløf's novel *The Wonderful Adventures of Nils*.

Published early in the twentieth century, the novel tells the story of Sweden's history and geography. It was written for children but became one of the most popular Swedish books of the last hundred years. Lagerløf covers all the different parts of Sweden except Halland, an area in the south-west. Many people believe she omitted Halland because she saw it as 'racially impure' – Lagerløf was involved in (and financially supported) racial biology research in its early stages. This second part features a new music track called 'It's Grim Out West' by Dan Ola Persson, whose background is in Scandinavian black and death metal.

The work's central theme is censorship: Lagerløf 'censored' Halland; Keller was censored for political reasons and accused of plagiarism (for *The Frost King*, written when she was 11 years old); Salinger 'censored' himself – he continued to write but did not publish after 1964, and refused all adaptations of his work.

Patrick Henry

Supported by

Courtesy of the artist

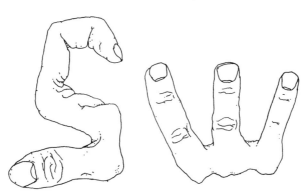

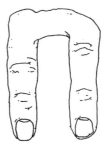

FACT (Foundation for Art and Creative Technology)

88 Wood Street, L1 4DQ
Galleries Open: Monday–Saturday 11.00–18.00, Sunday 12.00– 18.00
FACT Centre Open: Monday–Saturday 10.00–23.00, Sunday 11.00–22.30
Tel: +44 (0) 151 707 4464   www.fact.co.uk
Free Entry   Fully Accessible

Mother Touch

The artists' work selected for *Touched* at FACT examines the impression of one body, state or situation on another. If the ultimate touch is the conjoined biological material of mother and foetus, the inevitable anxiety of separation offers the most fundamental metaphor of things coming apart, moving away, coming back together – touching.

This memory of being touched is carried with us through life, as is the sense of parting, and the tension between those sensations is where meaning is often created. As more of us live at a distance from the family of origin, dispersed in other cities and overseas, inevitably the imprint of touch becomes more significant as we learn new virtualised ways to be touched and touch.

It was clear from conversations with all the artists selected for *Touched* at FACT that the relationship with their own place of birth and mother had strong resonances. It is the sense of trust, instilled at a young age, that enables artists to carve out their own meaning through experiments in time and space. Watch a baby test out proximity and distance, part of the preparation for independence later in life. Unconditional love has been fundamental

to many of the works commissioned and displayed here, nowhere more so than in the iconic work of Tehching Hsieh.

How did Hsieh have the strength of mind to complete his year-long performances and at the same time be planning the next performance, which would follow immediately after? Perhaps to prove it could be done, to posit a big question about life and time, or simply to see what happened. Whatever the motivation, Hsieh manifests a fundamental questioning of the value of time and identity, challenging us creatures of habit in our complacency.

Minouk Lim and Yves Netzhammer share concerns about separation and loss, with an anger and compulsion that demonstrates communication beyond language. For Minouk, a punk aesthetic is aimed at mindless redevelopment and the state, while Yves takes a phenomenological approach to things falling apart. Meanwhile, Kaarina Kaikkonen takes the original inspiration for her works from her childhood memories, her mother and father, and the smell of cleanly washed and dirty clothes.

The breakdown of communication is emphasised in the video work of Meiro Koizumi. Dislocation and the fetishisation of relationships underlie his work, nowhere more so than in *My Voice Would Reach You*, an idealised telephone call to mother that falls on deaf ears – a call centre employee trying to make sense of the caller's romantic request to share a holiday in the country together.

There is a Japanese expression about different types of snow yielding to different weights of step. The imprint is of course contextual – different people, states and materials can offer different pressures of touch, but what binds us together is our increasing need to find new ways to be touched, whether in body, spirit or mind, and to remember what being touched feels like.

Mike Stubbs

FACT
Gallery floor plans

Ground Floor

Entrance

café

Kaarina Kaikkonen

Stairs up

Tehching Hsieh

Lifts

Meiro Koizumi

Minouk Lim

Main entrance

First Floor

Stairs down

Lifts

Yves Netzhammer

Tehching Hsieh
One Year Performance 1980–1981, 1980–81

16mm film, time cards, photographs, time clock and other documentation materials
Courtesy of the artist and Sean Kelly Gallery, New York

7

Tehching Hsieh's work, informed through a period spent in New York City without a visa, experiments with time. He was actively 'wasting his time' by setting up a stringent set of conditions within five different year-long performances. The driving force for an individual to perform such extreme actions must surely be the ultimate cipher for being emotionally, psychologically touched – and that, ultimately, is a gift. His work poses the question: as humans how can we afford *not* to be touched?

An artist who has been mythologised since retiring from making art in 2000, this is the first exhibition of Hsieh's work in the UK. The exhibition focuses on documentation of his performance 'life work', *One Year Performance 1980–1981*. For one year, the artist punched a worker's time clock located in his studio, on the hour, every hour. Marking the occasion by taking a self-portrait on a single frame of 16mm film, the resulting reel documents a year in his life at approximately one second per day – a pace that is the polar opposite of the enduring length of the original performance. The punch cards, witnessed by a third party for authenticity, and other ephemera document Hsieh's life restructured around this highly repetitive task.

Heather Corcoran and Mike Stubbs

© 1981, Tehching Hsieh

ONE YEAR PERFORMANCE
by *SAM HSIEH*

Open to public on dates circled from 11:00 a.m. to 5:00 p.m.

1980 to 1981

APR	1 2 3 4 5 6 7 8 9 10 ⑪ 12 13 14 15 16 17 18 19 20 21 22 23 24 25 ㉖ 27 28 29 30
MAY	1 2 3 4 5 6 7 8 9 10 11 12 13 14 15 16 17 18 19 20 21 22 23 24 25 26 27 28 29 30 ㉛
JUNE	1 2 3 4 5 6 7 8 9 10 11 12 13 14 15 16 17 18 19 20 21 22 23 24 25 26 ㉗ 29 30
JULY	1 2 3 4 5 6 7 8 9 10 11 12 13 14 15 16 17 18 19 20 21 22 23 24 25 ㉖ 27 28 29 30 31
AUG	1 2 3 4 5 6 7 8 9 10 11 12 13 14 15 16 17 18 19 20 21 22 23 24 25 26 27 28 29 ㉚ 31
SEPT	1 2 3 4 5 6 7 8 9 10 11 12 13 14 15 16 17 18 19 20 21 22 23 24 25 26 ㉗ 28 29 30
OCT	1 2 3 4 5 6 7 8 9 10 11 12 13 14 15 16 17 18 19 20 21 22 23 24 ㉕ 26 27 28 29 30 31
NOV	1 2 3 4 5 6 7 8 9 10 11 12 13 14 15 16 17 18 19 20 21 22 23 24 25 26 27 28 ㉙ 30
DEC	1 2 3 4 5 6 7 8 9 10 11 12 13 14 15 16 17 18 19 20 21 22 23 24 25 26 ㉗ 28 29 30 31
JAN	1 2 3 4 5 6 7 8 9 10 11 12 13 14 15 16 17 18 19 20 21 22 23 24 25 26 27 28 29 30 ㉛
FEB	1 2 3 4 5 6 7 8 9 10 11 12 13 14 15 16 17 18 19 20 21 22 23 24 25 26 27 ㉘
MAR	1 2 3 4 5 6 7 8 9 10 11 12 13 14 15 16 17 18 19 20 21 22 23 24 25 26 27 ㉘ 29 30 31
APR	1 2 3 4 5 6 7 8 9 10 ⑪ 12 13 14 15 16 17 18 19 20 21 22 23 24 25 26 27 28 29 30

CLOSING PERFORMANCE: APRIL 11 1981 AT 6:00 P.M.

111 HUDSON ST. 2FL N.Y.C. 10013

Kaarina Kaikkonen
Hanging On to Each Other, 2010

Collected used clothing

Finnish artist Kaarina Kaikkonen creates site-specific installations in both interior and exterior spaces using old pieces of clothing or shoes collected from local donors. The garments carry personal memories of the owner, and with them she makes large-scale architectural forms or sculptures. While the materials she uses represent a common experience of domestic life, they also often allude to the artist's own parents, as she uses her deceased father's jackets as well as her mother's shoes.

In this new project, Kaikkonen collects second-hand clothing from individuals of all ages from around the Liverpool city region, and installs them in FACT's public atrium. The maternal act of doing laundry can be understood as a basic symbol of healing, care and unconditional love – the tender care a mother devotes to washing dirty clothes for her family.

Heather Corcoran and Mike Stubbs

'Countless works and installations I have built, creating spaces within spaces. Through my work I try to understand myself more clearly – to understand where the internal ends and the external begins.'
Kaarina Kaikkonen

Kaarina Kaikkonen's work is curated in partnership with Asher Remy-Toledo and No Longer Empty. Supported by FRAME Finnish Fund for Art Exchange.

Courtesy of the artist

Minouk Lim
The Weight of Hands, 2010

HD video and sound, single-channel projection, 10 min
Supported by Arts Council Korea and SAMUSO, Seoul
Courtesy of the artist and Gallery PLANT, Seoul
Commissioned by FACT and Liverpool Biennial 2010 for *Touched*

In Minouk Lim's previous video works, *New Town Ghost* and *S.O.S.*, she compares 'before and after' images of specific sites within the development-crazed city of Seoul. She invents indirect strategies and symbols to discuss these fundamental and often sensitive issues – the first using movement (that of a flatbed truck moving throughout the city), the second light (that of a cruise ship spotlight on a river bank). While video is her main format, her work is heavily performance-based, constructing poetic yet contentious scenarios that hijack the city. In this new piece, the artist relies on temperature as a strategy.

In a combination of live art documentation, performance work and road trip movie, the video tracks the journey of a strange tourist group in a place of 'restricted access'. The project started as an attempt to use an infrared camera that picks up heat to penetrate the private, restricted sites of new developments that are carried out for public purposes. This heat-sensitive camera is usually used for surveillance or police operations: in this way, the video hijacks the instruments of surveillance.

In the video's narrative, a tour bus arrives at a development which the public cannot enter. The tour bus is denied access. In response, a woman starts a performance inside the bus as a gesture of resistance. Climbing up on the seats and singing, these special tourists hold their hands up towards the woman to elevate her. Here and throughout the film, hands are shown by infrared as tangible and tactile heat: while often deployed to block the camera lens by authorities who do not wish to be filmed, hands also become a metaphor for resistance, empowerment and recollection. As the woman's body flows around the bus, the places of 'restricted access' outside the window – construction sites and ghost apartments – are also sensed by heat. The result is a video that plays extensively with light and colour.

Set against the backdrop of a tourism-led development project in Korea – the Four Major Rivers Project, to which public authorities violently restrict access by groups and individuals opposed to it – the video is critical as well as experimental.

Heather Corcoran and Mike Stubbs

7

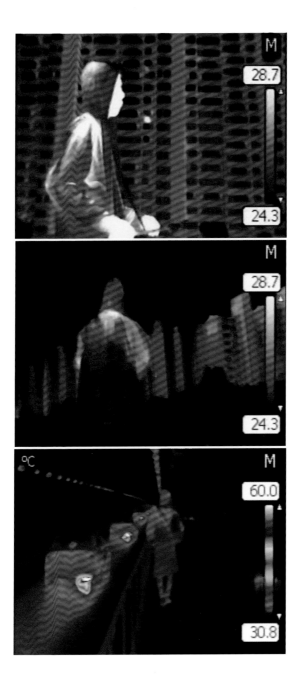

127

Meiro Koizumi

My Voice Would Reach You (single channel version), 2009

HD video installation, 16 min 45 sec

7

Dislocation and the fetishisation of relationships underlie the work of Meiro Koizumi, and especially so in *My Voice Would Reach You*. In a video documenting a performance of sorts, a male protagonist makes an idealised telephone call that falls on deaf ears. While the man pours out his thoughts and emotions to his mother, against the backdrop of a busy Tokyo street, a call centre employee is revealed to be desperately trying to make sense of what she is hearing on the other end – a romantic request to share a spa holiday in the country together, a particular gesture in Japanese culture to signify wealth. As the video progresses, the protagonist continues to make heartfelt 'prank calls' in an attempt to communicate his feelings to these surrogates, reaching out to his mother too late.

Reflecting on both the estrangement of life in the city and the folly of modern familial relationships, Koizumi contrasts humour with heartfelt emotion to create an absurd scenario that is compounded by the lead actor's own experience of losing his mother. Here and in his other work, he uses video in a way that documents performances, conversations and constructed scenarios to explore the psychology of urban relationships and modern living.

Heather Corcoran and Mike Stubbs

Courtesy of the artist

Commissioned by Mori Art Museum
Courtesy of Dicksmith Gallery & Annet Gelink Gallery

Yves Netzhammer

Dialogical Abrasion, 2010

3D animation, sculptural installation, sound
Courtesy of the artist and Anita Beckers Gallery, Frankfurt
Commissioned by FACT and Liverpool Biennial 2010 for *Touched*

7

Yves Netzhammer reflects on fundamental, even subconscious, aspects of the human condition. In this newly commissioned piece, he pares human figures back to their most basic forms in a narrative whose non-linear storyline suggests a flashback following an accident. A three-dimensional animation focuses on characters who are struggling to remember situations that are lost or strangely misshapen by the collective consciousness. Objects are out of place and mutating – in a moment of clarity, they adopt a symbolic meaning that quickly morphs to a new meaning, rarely fixed. Using highly simplified forms, his animations create a wordless, dream-like universe where the viewer is challenged to interpret and associate the situations presented. Underpinning this work is a desire to explore the philosophical and psychological relationship between humans and objects through a phenomenological approach.

In FACT's Gallery 2, his animation is set in a site-specific sculptural installation. Objects drawn from the animation are realised in three dimensions, in a similarly concise yet incongruous aesthetic. Splitting the gallery into two layers – 'above' and 'below' – the audience's movement is restricted by a labyrinth of 'trenches', where symbolic meaning is revealed from various perspectives. The result is an eerie effect whereby objects are not quite what they seem; an immersive space where the laws of existence are not obvious. A soundscape by collaborator and composer Bernd Schurer draws the viewer further into this universe.

Heather Corcoran and Mike Stubbs

Supported by

CALOUSTE GULBENKIAN FOUNDATION   swiss arts council pro helvetia   swiss cultural fund in britain   STANLEY THOMAS JOHNSON FOUNDATION

Courtesy of the artist

A Foundation Liverpool

67 Greenland Street, L1 0BY
Open: Tuesday–Sunday 11.00–18.00
Tel: +44 (0) 151 706 0600   www.afoundation.org.uk/liverpool
Free Entry   Fully Accessible

I am always touched by your presence dear
Floating past the evidence of possibilities
We could navigate together, psychic frequencies
Coming into contact with outer entities
We could entertain each one with our theosophies.
Blondie 1977

Surely nothing is better than being diverted by uncanny connections and the feedback loops that overpower our senses? I imagine Blondie stubbing out a fag and turning the pages of her copy of the *Phenomenology of Perception*. She is wearing the same caramel-coloured dress and socks she wore on the *Old Grey Whistle Test*. She thinks about her role in *Videodrome* and the contamination of reality through hallucinogenic media. Or maybe she does not. What else does an artist think about?

Between narrative and philosophy lies the text of interpretation. The labels on the gallery wall notoriously flatten out messy ideas into safe pockets of information. The thoughts of artists are so often obscure and stretch words into figures of ridicule. But it is the ideas of artists and the way they shape our perception of the world that we should attend to in this preface to an exhibition. It is the things we call ideas that artists manipulate to affect our senses.

We have chosen two artists who in very distinct ways push the limits of reality to expose the world as nothing but a representation, an illusionary place into which we are invited at our own risk. The wager is we will return from their worlds unscathed but perhaps slightly shaken. These artists make work so you don't have to. You would not want to build islands out of sandbags in the freezing sea. You would not want to spend hours performing a task so minimal that it makes most production-line routines appear luxurious in contrast.

Both artists totally inhabit the world in which they perform and become frames through we are invited to reconsider how an artwork might touch us. Each allows temporality itself to become critical once again, not only as a challenge to the materiality and exaggerated materialism of the art market, but as a mirror to a society increasingly aware of different temporal scales, such as the instantaneity of history after 9/11 and the slow arrival of ecological catastrophe.

Mark Waugh

Gallery floor plan

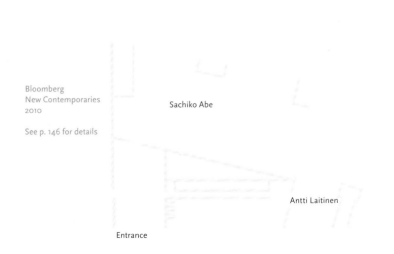

Bloomberg
New Contemporaries
2010

See p. 146 for details

Sachiko Abe

Antti Laitinen

Entrance

Sachiko Abe
Cut Papers, 2010

14

New commission by A Foundation and Liverpool Biennial 2010 for *Touched*

Sachiko Abe's work encompasses performance, drawing, film and sculptural installations using cut papers accumulated over the last seven years. Her practice explores duration, repetition and constraints. This is a paradox, as she first started creating artworks after leaving the Self-Defense Forces in Japan because 'the life of artists seemed so free'.

Her work since 1997 has explored the regimes of subjectivity that are imposed by society, most explicitly in her series of performance works, *Elevator Girl Friend*, in which she contravened the conventional behaviour of the demure elevator assistants employed by big department stores. Abe comments: 'While the job sounds boring, it was a "dream job" for young girls because it was believed then that only the most beautiful and elegant person could be assigned to be an elevator girl.'

Her more recent works continue to explore disquieting routines that provoke anxiety and touch us in ways we cannot explain. *Cut Papers* is a series of works that create a surplus of meaning within an apparently simple aesthetic economy. In *Cut Papers* Abe invites the audience to experience an intimate space in which the constant snipping of scissor blades is the only measure of time passing.

For *Touched* Abe performs for the duration of the Biennial. 'Be warned,' Abe says, 'my work is neither beautiful nor meditational.' Rather, it's an aesthetic paradox that locates the artist at the centre of a field of reciprocal subjectivity: she is an object of the gaze that returns the subject to him- or herself, by activating a feedback loop. It is this scenic space of perception and production that is the focus of the work.

Abe presents the performance in an environment of large-scale sculptural interventions in A Foundation's Furnace Gallery, along with a new large-scale drawing work produced earlier (during her 2010 residency with A Foundation funded by the Pola Foundation). Intensive durational periods of drawing produce an intricate graphic weave, perhaps best approached through the dimension of 'the fold' as expressed by French philosopher Gilles Deleuze. Like *Cut Papers*, Abe's drawings invite us to contemplate the intensity of ideas that accumulate and are disseminated in the transformation of a white sheet of paper into a medium of communication.

Mark Waugh

Supported by

Courtesy of the artist

Antti Laitinen

The Bark, 2010

14

New commission by A Foundation and Liverpool Biennial 2010 for *Touched*

Antti Laitinen works across idioms of performance, video and photography. His mission across this collection of idioms is to stage mythologies and erase the boundary between success and failure, through a trajectory of personal endurance and almost delusional imagination. Laitinen takes us beyond normality into a new reality at once both innocent and yet haunted by the knowledge of our contemporary ecological crisis. He encapsulates an artistic vision that explores the imperfect resolution of the world when faced with the sublime limits of our imagination. He says of his work: 'It is more important to struggle for your dreams than succeed in them.' The critic Peter Suchin suggests: 'The term "authentic" is so deeply embedded in the ideology of the artist that to suggest Laitinen moves away from the special world that this word implies may seem to some a heretical assertion. It is, rather, a point of criticality to raise questions around received ideas about art and the special status of the artist, and in this respect Laitinin's work is, surprisingly, a type of realism. The more absurd it looks, the more real, in a certain sense, it is, a man like any other man carrying out in a painstaking fashion extremely demanding tasks.'

For A Foundation, Laitinen presents a survey of key works from the last decade of his performances, including the *It's My Island* trilogy, *Bare Necessities*, *Untitled* and *Walk the Line*, among others. He also presents a new commission for *Touched*. This new work involves the building of a vessel in the gallery at Greenland Street and an inaugural voyage. *The Bark* is a boat made from ancient bark collected from the floor of the forest. It has both metaphorical and material qualities. It can transport us from the place of origin to somewhere else far away. In this story the bark will be transported by boat from Finland to England and then made into a vessel that will transport the artist on a voyage across the Mersey.

Mark Waugh

Courtesy of the artist

Supported by

 CALOUSTE GULBENKIAN FOUNDATION

 FRAME Finnish Fund for Art Exchange

 EMBASSY OF FINLAND LONDON

THE FINNISH INSTITUTE IN LONDON

John Moores Painting Prize
The Walker Art Gallery

William Brown Street, L3 8EL
Open: daily 10.00–17.00
Tel: 0151 478 4199   www.liverpoolmuseums.org.uk/johnmoores
Free entry   Fully accessible

The *John Moores Painting Prize* has a reputation for defining the shifts and trends in one of the most enduring mediums of all, paint. Now, in its fifty-third year the competition boasts a roll call of esteemed winners, including David Hockney and Richard Hamilton, who went on to find fame and acclaim after winning the prize, and Peter Doig, who described winning the John Moores in 1993 as a pivotal moment in his career.

Almost 3,000 entrants submitted work in the hope of winning the first prize of £25,000. Forty-five works are included in the exhibition, known for spotting rising talent.

The jurors for this year's competition form a strong team of experience and expertise, with former Royal Academy Exhibitions Secretary Sir Norman Rosenthal joined by contemporary artists Goshka Macuga and Gary Hume, Liverpool-born artist Ged Quinn and painter Alison Watt.

Reyahn King, director of galleries, National Museums Liverpool, said:

'What's so special about this painting competition is that anyone can enter. We have the best established artists alongside emerging talent. Today's prizewinners really are the future stars of the art world.

The illustrious history and ongoing vigour of the John Moores make this the country's most important contemporary painting prize.

Paintings submitted can be very different. We receive the strange, striking, unusual, the exciting. But they all have one thing in common – they depict a time and a moment in contemporary British art.'

Don't miss this year's prize winner announcement streamed live from the Walker Art Gallery on the evening of Thursday 16 September 2010 at www.liverpoolmuseums.org.uk/johnmoores

A partnership between national Museums Liverpool and John Moores Liverpool Exhibition Trust

Supported by

Courtesy of Simon Webb, 2008

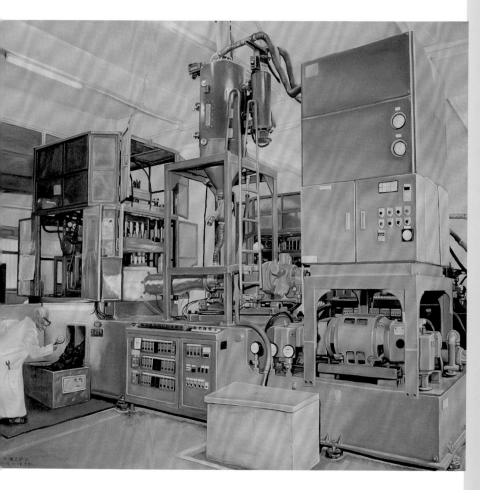

Zou Tao
Excrement Factory

Wolfgang Tillmans
The Walker Art Gallery

A

William Brown Street, L3 8EL
18 September–12 December
Open: daily 10.00–17.00
Tel: 0151 478 4199   www.liverpoolmuseums.org.uk
Free entry   Fully accessible

This exhibition features nine photographic works by German photographer Wolfgang Tillmans, dating from 2004 to 2009, recently acquired by the Arts Council, as well as a number of works from Tillmans' own collection.

The photographs will be displayed as installations and interventions, curated by Tillmans, around the permanent collection displays in the Walker Art Gallery.

The installations reflect the artist's very personal response to the Walker Art Gallery's distinguished permanent collection, drawing out connections between his own work and traditional genres such as still life, landscape and portraiture. His selection ranges across a broad span of art history, including the gallery's medieval and renaissance collection, a painting by one of Liverpool's most famous artists, George Stubbs, and contemporary masters, such as Patrick Caulfield.

The Walker Art Gallery's head of fine art, Ann Bukantas, says:

'For Wolfgang Tillmans, the installation functions as a work of art in its own right. Through his interventions he invites us to consider the relationship between artworks and the locations in which they are found, rather than simply looking at the artwork as self-contained.

Tillmans is one of the most exciting and innovative artists of his generation, so we are thrilled to be showing his work during the Liverpool Biennial and we are very grateful to the Arts Council Collection for making it possible to bring such an important group of works to the Walker Art Gallery.'

Wolfgang Tillmans
Dan, 2008
C-type print, edition 6/10 + 1 AP, 40 x 30 cm

Supported by

ArtFund®   Supported by ARTS COUNCIL ENGLAND

Bloomberg
newcontemporaries 2010

A Foundation, 7 Greenland Street, L1 0BY
Open: Tuesday–Sunday 12.00–18.00
Tel: +44 (0) 151 706 0600   www.afoundation.org.uk/liverpool
Free Entry   Fully Accessible

'The future is with *New Contemporaries*... the national panorama it presents feels more engaging and urgent than ever.'
Evening Standard 2009

'The best means of seeing what is going on in up-and-coming artists' studios across the UK.'
The Guardian 2009

New Contemporaries (formerly *Young Contemporaries*) dates back to the first exhibition of graduates from Greater London Art Schools in 1949. Throughout the subsequent sixty years of its existence, it has identified serious artists from each generation and given them a platform from which to launch their careers. The premise remains as effective today as then.

The list of alumni includes David Hockney, Frank Auerbach, Paula Rego, R.B. Kitaj, Damien Hirst, Peter Doig, and Bob and Roberta Smith. Participants are selected through a rigorous process that is open and democratic by a panel of influential arts figures, predominantly artists who have themselves often previously exhibited in *New Contemporaries*. The selectors for 2010 are Mexican artist Gabriel Kuri, Turner prize-winner Mark Leckey and painter Dawn Mellor.

This year, the show will feature the work of 49 artists across a range of media, providing visitors with a unique opportunity to engage with new and emergent practice and ideas from across the UK.

Participating artists 2010:
Greta Alfaro, Holly Antrum, Caline Aoun, Johann Arens, Ed Atkins, Nick Bailey, Nathan Barlex, Melis Van den Berg, Alice Browne, Amir Chasson, Joe Clark, Matthew Coombes, Patrick Coyle, Keren Dee, Sophie Eagle, Claas Gutsch, Guy Haddon-Grant, Jessica Harris, Rowena Harris, Emma Hart, Darren Harvey-Regan, Raphael Hefti, Ian Homerston, Chris Hughes, Rowena Hughes, Vasileios Kantas, Krister Klassman, Sam Knowles, Alec Kronacker, Agnieszka Kucharko, Dan Lichtman, Agata Madejska, Russell Maurice, Ella McCartney, Nick Mobbs, Murray O'Grady, Chloe Ostmo, Sion Parkinson, Peles Empire, Laure Provost, Kristian de la Riva, Kiwoun Shin, Theodoros Stamatogiannis, Sue Tarbitten, Edward Thomasson, Naomi Uchida, Mark Walker, Pablo Wendel, Joel Wyllie

The exhibition will later be shown at the ICA in London.

Supported by

Supported by
ARTS COUNCIL ENGLAND

Rowena Hughes
City (Split Penrose Series), 2009
screenprint on inkjet print of found image
44 x 32 cm

B

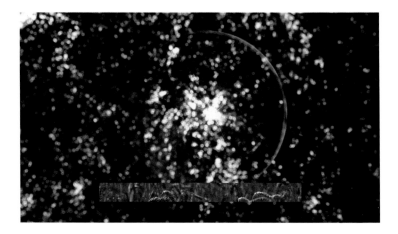

Ed Atkins
A Thousand Centuries of Death [video still], 2009
HD video
6 min 41 sec

>
Nick Mobbs
Red Leather Sofa, 2009
screenprint
132 x 99 cm

\<CityStates\>

Novas Contemporary Urban Centre
41–51 Greenland Street, L1 0BS
18 September–28 November
Open: Tuesday–Saturday: 11.00–18.00
Sunday: 11.00–16.00
Tel: +44 (0)151 708 3529   www.contemporaryurbancentre.org

City States is a new collaboration between Novas Scarman Contemporary Urban Centre Liverpool and Liverpool Biennial for the 2010 Biennial festival. The Grade II listed warehouse has been converted to be a vibrant cultural and community centre at the heart of the Baltic Triangle, including a restaurant, café, bar, cinema, conference facilities and performance and gallery space. The building provides the ideal context in which to show contemporary art from cities around the world, and introduce the artists, organising bodies and audiences to the fabulous opportunities provided by the Centre to local people.

City States is an exhibition of art focused on life in cities around the world. The greatest challenges faced by humanity are in the cities, where the majority of the population now lives. City-to-city learning is the quickest and most effective way of addressing these challenges. *City States* consists of a cluster of seven international exhibitions, initiated and wholly supported by embassies, foreign governments, international agencies or galleries, that explore the cultural dynamics between cities and states.

In 2008, Liverpool Biennial received nearly half a million visitors over the ten-week festival, generating £26.3m for the local economy. By bringing seven high-quality exhibitions under one roof, in a unified, central space, *City States* provides a major draw for visitors and an opportunity to relax and use the excellent facilities offered by Novas CUC Liverpool, as well as placing the Baltic Triangle more firmly on the map for residents and visitors to the city alike.

Liverpool Biennial as an arts agency works to create learning at the point where the local and the international meet. The social benefits are felt through increased community confidence and capacity, and we see it as of the utmost importance that *City States*, in addition to bringing economic benefits through increased spend in the building, will enable local people to take advantage of the opportunity provided by the presence of artists and art organisations from around the world to create their own networks and give form to their own aspirations.

Susie Parsons, Interim Chief Executive,
Novas Scarman Group

City States
Gallery floor plans

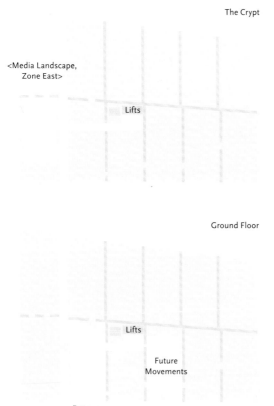

The Crypt

<Media Landscape, Zone East>

Lifts

Ground Floor

Lifts

Future Movements

Entrance

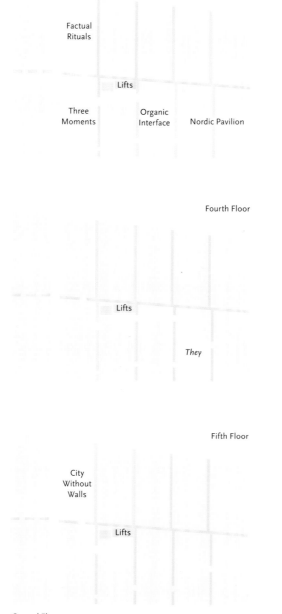

Third Floor

Factual
Rituals

Lifts

Three
Moments

Organic
Interface

Nordic Pavilion

Fourth Floor

Lifts

They

Fifth Floor

City
Without
Walls

Lifts

Ground Floor

<Media Landscape, Zone East>
The Crypt

There is today a rapid growth of new cities across the globe, notably in the Far East. Cities are the sites where heterogeneous groups meet and exchange creative ideas. It is often cities rather than nations that capture the curiosity of contemporary artists, although we cannot, of course, think of cities without considering their host countries.

<Media Landscape, Zone East>, one of the projects forming part of *City States*, features a group of artists working internationally in locations from Seoul, Tokyo, Beijing, Taipei and Singapore to New York, Düsseldorf and London. Seoul, representing South Korea, invited ten Korean artists and nominated 12 other artists, from Japan, China, Taiwan, Hong Kong, Vietnam, Indonesia and Singapore, to take part in the project. While all the artists come from Asian cultures, their stories encompass both their native identities and their new experiences of different cultures from across the world. They often move between different cities and subsequently transfer their art to the other side of the world, with correspondingly fresh stimuli to their imaginations.

The high-tech evolution of the 21st century has brought new social trends that impact on the sensibilities and minds of today. Globalisation has expedited interaction and instant communication across different cultures, and has generated hybridism, especially in the art world. Identifying art in terms of fixed genres now appears to be inadequate, and 'interdisciplinarity' is a more fruitful paradigm. For media art, whether film, video, animation or performance, traditional inflexible boundaries of genre are now less meaningful than they used to be.

In this exhibition we focus on 'moving images', showcasing newly released works by artists working with various media and methods reflecting their reinterpretation of new media art. This offers an excellent opportunity to experience the emerging dynamism of Asian media art as well as to explore a new understanding of 'moving images'.

A parallel project will follow in October 2010 at the Korean Cultural Centre UK, located in central London. The show will showcase the same collection of works, but presented in a new format. More information will be available soon at www.kccuk.org.uk.

Curated by Stephanie Seungmin Kim and Jinsuk Suh. Nominators: Leng Lin, Eugene Tan

Supported by

Mioon
Statue Number, 2010
HD Video / Multichannel Video Installation

Future Movements
Ground floor

C

Future Movements features artworks that draw inspiration from the city of Jerusalem and its changing urban structure. The exhibition takes the viewer to places outside the spiritual and holy Old City to urban locations that, despite their importance in shaping the contemporary urban city, have rarely been referenced or addressed in literature and visual art.

14 artists have been invited; Basel Abbas and Ruanne Abou Rahme (Palestine), Jawad Al Malhi (Palestine), Sarah Beddington (UK), Anna Boggon (UK), CAMP Group (India), Raouf Haj Yihya (Palestine), Alexandra Handal (Palestine/ UK), Shuruq Harb (Palestine), Maj Hasager (Denmark), Jakob Jakobsen (Denmark), Bouchra Khalili (Morocco/ France), Larissa Sansour (Palestine/ Denmark) and Oraib Toukan (Jordan)

The exhibition unravels Jerusalem as an urban structure in all its physical, social, economic and political complexity, demonstrating how urban space is divided, conquered, abandoned and occupied again.

Future Movements is curated by Samar Martha and organised by ArtSchool Palestine in cooperation with Al Hoash Gallery, Jerusalem, and Visiting Arts.

Supported by the Barjeel Art Foundation, the Danish Arts Council, Foundation for Arts Initiative, Zina Jardaneh, the Palestinian Ministry of Culture and Visiting Arts.

Supported by

ArtSchool Palestine
منتدى الفنون للمعاصرة

barjeel بارجيل

BROWNBOOK

FfAI

ff
Ford Foundation

Contemporary Practices
VISUAL ARTS FROM THE MIDDLE EAST

حوش الفن الفلسطيني
Palestinian Art Court - al Hoash

Ministry of Culture

oasis

STATENS KUNSTRÅD
DANISH ARTS COUNCIL

Visiting Arts

Larissa Sansour
A Space Exodus (video still), 2009
Single channel video, 3 min
Courtesy of Galerie La B.A.N.K., Paris

The Nordic Pavilion
Third floor

The eight artists chosen for NICE's *Nordic Pavilion* find inspiration from urban landscapes, social environments, identities, rhythms in movement and fetishised commodities. These imaginative geographies help us to look at our own ritualised ways of living, everyday experiences of the city's environment, and the materials with which we identify ourselves.

Norwegian-born artist Knut Åsdam investigates patterns of behaviour, with a particular focus on theories of disorder and social pathologies that are impacted upon by urban environments and architecture. The artist's new film will be given its world premiere at *City States*.

Reflecting on the notion of urbanism, artist Søren Thilo Funder (Denmark) draws influence from the city environment with sociological references to dystopian societies, sci-fi and counter-culture. His film *Council of Citizens* (2010) presents a local council where residents engage in tightly orchestrated ritualised dance.

Hrafnhildur Arnardottir AKA 'Shoplifter' (Iceland) explores the use and symbolic nature of hair. She is well known for her collaborative work with the singer and actress Björk, who has often worn her hair sculptures. Her obsession has evolved into an exploration of human hair's significance to visual and material culture. Another Icelandic artist also featured is Hrafnkell Sigurðsson, with his film *7x7* (2008). The work emerges out of our relationship with nature and industrialised landscapes.

Marianna Mørkøre and Rannvá Káradóttir (Faroe Islands) exhibit their award-winning film *Memotech* (2009) and new film *Magma* (2010), shot on super 8; the films explore the contrast between minimalist movement and the overwhelming and extreme landscape of the Faroe Islands.

In his films and installations Kalle Brolin (Sweden) creates staged situations that create tension between truth and fiction, reality and invention, history and present-day situations. The *Story Café* project by Johanna Lecklin (Finland) has been delivered in 11 locations and seven countries to date. Visitors are able to record their own stories, which are archived and presented in the café, but are also able to view past participants' stories that have been dramatised by Johanna to create new narratives.

Nordic Pavilion is curated by Claudia Lastra in collaboration with NICE (Nordic Intercultural Creative Events).

Supported by

  THE FINNISH INSTITUTE IN LONDON   NICe

Hrafnhildur Arnardottir AKA 'Shoplifter'
Gloria, A Study for an Opera II, 2010
Image courtesy of Hrafnhildur Arnardottir

Organic Interface
Third floor

C

CANCELLED

Organic Interface brings together eight artists – Chen Chih-Chien, Lin Kun-Ying, Hou I-Ting, Wu Cheng-Chang, Chuang Yi-Lang, Liu Yin-Sheng, Fu Wen-Chien and Lee Mei-Yi. The artists present perspectives on individual life and the urbanised homeland, figuring out the puzzle of aesthetic power through digital content.

In the contemporary international context constructed by globalisation in the 21st century, the cultural subjectivity of Taiwan requires a more expressive avatar and imaginative embodiment for its own innovative localised images, which characterise traditional Chinese thinking. Five hundred years of Western imperialism, with its powerful distortion of Eastern cultural beliefs into a rigid pattern of all-natures-in-one-unity, has damaged local culture and also twisted the overall aesthetic relationship between the individual and the universe: that abstract, obscure, profound and intuitive umbilical cord for energy exchange.

We can place this intangible relationship in the avant-garde and subversive context of media technology development, which breeds a kind of ideological confrontation in the form of an 'organic interface' between East and West: the metaphysical existence of Taiwanese

cultural subjectivity is represented by the embodiment of visual images of the physical world. This is effective in challenging the Western sceptical analytical posture on epistemology.

Taking Taiwan New Media Art as the referential means to a historical break-point on the vertical timeline, what is about to happen is a retro avant-garde movement of authentic Chinese culture in terms of aesthetic relationships. On a macro scale, the Chinese Cultural Revolution (1966–76) resulted in a distortion of the social constitution of contemporary China, with the tension resulting from the antagonistic relationship between the People's Republic and Taiwan. Michael Foucault's concept of 'field of force' can offer us an imaginative space for debating Taiwanese cultural subjectivity as an organic interface reflecting authentic Chinese belief.

Incorporating this abstract theory of 'field of force' into the concept of 'organic interface' allows us to create a new domain, 'field of aesthetic power', through the combination of traditional Chinese cultural beliefs and avant-garde Western technology.

Chen Chih-Chien
Vision of Taiwan – Taihsi, 2009
Screen projection

Three Moments
The Bahamas, Barbados and Martinique Pavilion
Third floor

'How are we to write the histories of non-western societies in relation to modernity? Modernity is, as we know, an extremely slippery signifier, and appears here with as many quote marks as I can muster: and "the modern" in its many derivatives – early modern, late modern, post-modern, modernity, modernism – has long been effectively appropriated to the story of the west, monopolizing for western civilization the privilege of living to the full the potentialities of the present "from the inside". It is therefore difficult to imagine this story in any way other than as a binary polarity: modernity and its 'Others'. Only two narrative alternatives then seem possible. Either the story is told from within the perspective of modernity itself: in which case it is difficult to prevent it becoming a triumphalist narrative in which the "others" are permanently marginalized. Or one reorients the story within its margins, seeking by this move to reverse and disrupt the normalised order of things by bringing into visibility all that cannot be seen from, or is structurally obscured by, the usual vantage point.'

Stuart Hall, 'Modernity and Its Others: Three 'Moments' In The Post-war History of the Black Diaspora Arts',

In the groundbreaking essay 'Modernity and Its Others: Three "Moments" In The Post-war History of the Black Diaspora Arts', Stuart Hall revisits modernity through three historical art movements from the perspective of the Diaspora. This discourse stands as the theme of this pavilion where three moments will become symbolised by three Caribbean islands; the Bahamas, Martinique and Barbados.

The featured artists – Ewan Atkinson, Ishi Butcher, Akyem Ramsay, Kendra Frorup, Heino Schmid, John Beadle, Lynn Parotti, Lavar Munroe and Blue Curry (all from the Bahamas) and David Damoison, Christian Bertin and Jean-François Boclé from Martinique – were selected on their ability to make work that responds to contemporary and historical global themes. For the first time artists from the Caribbean region are collectively making new work that responds to the city of Liverpool while maintaining a distinctive stance on what Stuart Hall might call a 21st-century Caribbean modernist aesthetic.

Three Moments is selected and curated by Dominique Brebion (Martinique), Alissandra Cummins (Barbados), Holly Parotti (Bahamas) and Allison Thompson (Barbados) in collaboration with the ICF.

Supported by

Barbados Museum & Historical Society

RÉPUBLIQUE FRANÇAISE
Liberté • Égalité • Fraternité

Culture communication

Regional Directorate
Cultural Affairs
Martinique

aica
Caraïbe du sud
Internationale
International

www.aica-sc.net

NAGB
NATIONAL ART GALLERY
OF THE BAHAMAS

National Art Gallery Commission

Lavar Munroe
You Must be Wondering, What Type of
Creature Am I?, 2009
Graphite drawing, digital colour, Ultra Chrome K3 inks on velvet
paper (signed ed 1/1), 44" x 50"

Tactful Rituals
Third floor

C

Featuring artists; Annie Baillargeon, Martin Dufrasne / Carl Bouchard, Claudie Gagnon, Massimo Guerrera, Adad Hannah, Manon Labrecque, Catherine Sylvain, Julie Andrée T.

When faced with a simultaneously troubling and stimulating work of art, we can't help but be emotionally struck. Our feelings and bodies are stirred, moved. We're caught off balance in the here-now, connected with the artwork in a special way. However, something more than mere composure is impacting us in current contemporary art. Increasingly, current artworks are operating rooms in which the artist's body and actions have a meaning that the work both holds and expresses. The work is mobilised within actions, manoeuvres and performances that make it be and without which it could not exist. We have therefore united artists who, in the main, work on two fronts, 'plastic' art and related actions.

Here, photographs (Bouchard/Dufrasne, Baillargeon), videos (Labrecque, Hannah), body-based sculptures (Sylvain), installations that may or may not be linked to performance (Julie Andrée T., Gagnon) and the traces of manoeuvre-based contacts (Guerrera) allow echoes of the body and its materiality to resonate.

Whether through active prostheses (Labrecque), shaped and activated matter (Sylvain), actions catalysed through what's left of them (Guerrera) or cloned and organised into icons (Baillargeon), the body, in these ceremonials, is brought to life and put forward, evoked and tried, projected towards other bodies and the signs that represent it.

The exhibition *Tactful Rituals* shares in the stance of *City States*, proposing to look at a special aesthetic, different from Montréal's, which developed in Québec City and has radiated throughout the province. If the artists united here don't all work in Québec City, they are nonetheless influenced by its slant, because Québec City has been a forum for the exploration of context-based art that actively seeks viewer reaction, giving rise to more intrusive forms of performance: manoeuvres, happenings, situational constructions or, as Guy Debord wrote, 'concrete constructions of life's momentary ambiances, and their transformation into a superior positional quality'.[1]

1 Guy Debord, '*Rapport sur la construction de situations et sur les conditions de l'organisation et de l'action de la tendance situationniste internationale*', in *Œuvres* (Paris, Gallimard, 2006) p. 309.

Supported by

BRITISH COUNCIL — JUMP SHIP RAT — Québec — MANIF DART THE QUÉBEC CITY BIENNIAL

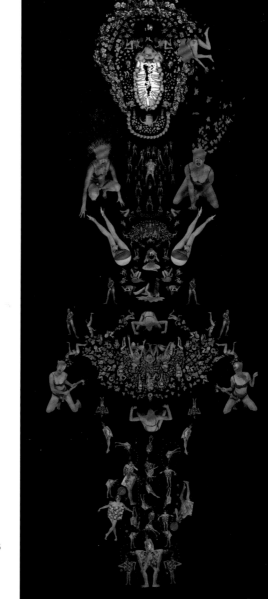

Annie Baillargeon
Orbite d'origines orgasmiques, 2006
Inkjet print on photo paper,
152.40 x 228.60 cm
Image courtesy of Annie Baillargeon

They
Karl-Heinz Klopf
Cinema, fourth floor

Screening times:
Saturdays: 12.00, 13.00, 14.00, 15.00, 16.00 , 17.00
Sundays: 12.00, 13.00, 14.00, 15.00

They is a film concerning a municipal area in North Liverpool, which has suffered an extreme drop in population. The area is one of the lowest socio-economic areas in England, which used to be an active, highly populated community but has mostly been demolished and replaced by an unused hilly park, which extends over much of the district. The surrounding neighbourhoods are fighting for the solidarity of their remaining communities and at the same time they are in search of a new identity and better conditions.

They precisely addresses this issue, whilst also developing its own narration, which leads to a more abstract and transformative approach to how the landscape of this place may be viewed. Karl-Heinz Klopf is interested in this hybrid exploration, which operates on many levels, and which allows him to discuss, and bring to light, complex, conflicting and sometimes obscure incidents.

Karl-Heinz Klopf was born in Linz, Austria. He studied at the University for Artistic and Industrial Design in Linz and currently lives and works in Vienna. His artistic practice is mainly concerned with constructed environments and the everyday life in the urban sphere. He works in different media such as drawing, video, photography, installations and projects in the context of architecture and urbanism.

They was produced following a six month residency in Liverpool as part of Urban Interventions, an artists exchange programme between Liverpool, Dortmund, Tallinn, Istanbul and Linz and commissioned by Liverpool Biennial. The project has been funded with support from the European Commission.

Supported by

austrian cultural forumˡᵒⁿ

Urban Interventions is part financed by the European Union

Education and Culture DG

Culture Programme

Karl-Heinz Klopf
They (production still)
35 min, colour, stereo

City Without Walls
Fifth floor

City Without Walls is an exhibition whose title draws on disparate sources: an Old Testament passage, a poem by W.H. Auden (1969) and Andre Malraux's 'museum without walls'. The exhibition's allusions are used as a foil for the Lithuanian capital of Vilnius. If Lithuania resides at the geopolitical nexus between the eastern periphery of the European Union and Belarus, Russia and beyond, then Vilnius is its cosmopolitan epicentre, whose cultural openness and diversity makes it metaphorically a 'city without walls'. Many artists spent formative time in Vilnius, only to later contribute to artistic developments in other cities, including the Cubist Jacques Lipchitz in Paris, the abstractionist Lasar Segall in São Paulo, and the Fluxus artist George Maciunas and experimental filmmaker Jonas Mekas in New York. Although these artists achieved prominence abroad, Vilnius was generative of their artistic ideas.

Like the Lithuanian artists that preceded them, the participants in City Without Walls embody international artistic sensibilities engendered by the Lithuanian capital's urbanity. Their work is dovetailed by formal heterogeneity, visual poetics, conceptual verve and the myriad themes they address. Laura Garbštienė, for

example, presents Film about Unknown Artist (2009). Her film concerns an unknown artist who visits memorial plate dedicated to another unknown artist (artwork by Konstantinas Bogdanas) in the backyard of Vilnius Art Academy; this leads the protagonist to travel to holy places in Lithuania to do penance. S&P Stanikas's contribution to the exhibition is Allergy to the Sun (Hannelore Kohl) (2010), a site-specific work that encompasses video and large-scale drawings whose foci revolve around the suicide of the photophobic wife of German Chancellor Helmut Kohl. Also working in installation, but with different formal strategies and narratives, is Žilvinas Landzbergas's Holy Promises (2010). Landzbergas's installation incorporates lightboxes and illuminated festoons, a simulated open fire, and tree trunks. Rounding out City Without Walls is Žilvinas Kempinas's Lemniscate (2008), a large-scale kinetic sculpture consisting of two massive industrial fans whose billowing force suspends a strip of magnetic tape in midair.

City Without Walls is curated by Raúl Zamudio and Laura Rutkutė with the assistance of Augustina Matusevičiūtė, and organised by VARTAI gallery, Vilnius.

Supported by

S&P Stanikas
Allergy to the Sun (Hannelore Kohl) (detail), 2010
Installation, graphite, paper, plexiglas, wood, 300 x 600cm

The **COOPERATIVE**

D

28–32 Renshaw Street, L1 4EF
18 September–29 November
Open: Wednesday–Saturday 13.00–19.00
Free entry

PORTFOLIO / PERFORMANCE / EXHIBITION / INTERACT

A melange of unpredictable happenings in electric, plastic, paint and brain-wave – The Cooperative space is easy to find with its hideous frontage and delightful location. And worth it.

This ambitious joint initiative is the first of its kind in the city. Seven of Liverpool's key permanent arts collectives – The Royal Standard, Jump Ship Rat, Mercy, Red Wire, Arena Studios & Gallery, Sound Network, and Lost Soul and Stranger Service Station – have gathered to conspire and provide new work and an innovative archive.

This is where you begin to negotiate the inner and outer worlds of Liverpool artists – and art itself. You are welcome to come and see what we do, in this festival and in our studios all year round. You are to bring what enthusiasm you can muster. You are going to really like The Cooperative.

This arts programme and creative hub is aimed at providing quality insight into the resident arts scene, and the work of top Liverpool-based curators, programmers and performers. The Cooperative also features a new façade installation by Parisian squatter-artist Yabon Paname and Jump Ship Rat, and a bespoke performance space by Mercy.

There will be special openings, discussions, workshops and performances every week. Sign up to twitter.com/thecoopscoops or catch our feed and link to our member sites:

http://mercyonline.co.uk/
http://www.theservicestation.co.uk/
http://www.the-royal-standard.com/
http://www.jumpshiprat.org/
http://www.arenastudiosgallery.com/
http://www.redwireredwire.com/
http://soundnetwork.org.uk/

The Cooperative

Supported by

Photo: Thomas Harold

S.Q.U.A.T.
LIVERPOOL 2010

All exhibitions open Tuesday–Saturday 14.00–18.00
Also opening 19 September and 25 September 12.00–19.00

SQUAT (Social Questioning Using Art Today) Liverpool is the umbrella title for the collaborative project between the New York-based group, No Longer Empty (NLE) and the UK-based group, The Art Organisation (TAO). SQUAT examines the issues of regeneration of empty commercial spaces by artistic communities. In Liverpool, SQUAT will zoom in on the Ropewalks and L1 area of Liverpool city centre.

Both NLE and TAO share an interest in the creative use of empty spaces. As economic certainties crumble around us, and the spaces we previously inhabited come into focus as the monument to or ruins of 'better times', how communities re-infiltrate or experiment with the spaces left following the commercial exodus could be the key to how we move forward.

Through various exhibitions, events, performances and interventions taking place at spaces generously donated by local landlords, SQUAT will breathe new life into forgotten buildings as residual and collective memory, new artistic experimentation and urban exploration and discovery collide.

No Longer Empty

The No Longer Empty (NLE) Liverpool Biennial Exhibition is curated and produced by Asher Remy-Toledo, who co-founded the group in New York with Manon Slome in response to the current economic crisis. Their mission is to introduce art to a wider public by temporarily transforming vacant spaces. Through the exhibitions NLE produce they encourage new models of collaboration between internationally renowned and lesser-known artists, curators, museums, grassroots organisations and generous landlords. Using limited resources, but without compromising on quality, NLE manages to shift the paradigm of how art is experienced, and, ultimately, who it is for. Liverpool marks the premiere of No Longer Empty on the Road before continuing on to other locations.

www.nolongerempty.com

The Art Organisation (TAO) Property Solutions

TAO, founded and run by Robert Howie Smith and Greg Scott-Gurner, has been active for the last ten years in helping to establish spaces and opportunities for artists and creative communities in Liverpool and across the UK by enabling the legal occupation of disused spaces.

TAO Property Solutions, based on Slater Street, launched in March this year and is the new branch of TAO established to take on the specific role of brokering this interaction. It enables a clear and confidential point of contact between owners and future tenants, maintaining portfolios of available spaces and potential projects.

www.theartorganisation.co.uk

Courtesy of Gregory Scott-Gurner

Wolstenholme Creative Space

11 Wolstenholme Square, L1 4JJ
Tel: 0151 324 1493

Album

18 September–17 October

This place has touched me, this memory will record me, you will shape me.

Album is an exhibition comprised of new and existing works by 17 artists currently on the Royal College of Art's Photography MA. Working across the disciplines of photography, film and video, new site-specific works, which seek to respond to the particularities of the surrounding area and Wolstenholme Creative Space (WCS), will also be produced.

Intrigued by the prospect of exhibiting in an unconventional gallery space, the decision to show at WCS was made by the group in order to allow reciprocity of influence to take place between the institution and the artist-led not-for-profit space.

Similarly, the site itself will, in hosting the collection, be subject to a process of transformation and re-reading

With These Walls We Are Shaped

28 October–28 November

The gallery's second contribution to the Biennial invites 12 artists selected by open submission – Michael Coombs (UK), Henrietta Simson (UK), David Eveleigh and Melissa Evans (UK), Su-Chen Hung (USA), Andrew Brookfield (UK), Junichrio Iwase (Canada), Ulrike Oeter (Germany), Cait Walker and Robin Heap (UK), Carol Ramsay (UK) and Hannah Wiles (UK) to create site-specific work within the gallery's crumbling walls. The building now inhabited by WCS has been around since the 1700s, when it was home to Liverpool's first mayor, and has been an artistic space since the 1990s. Nestled between two nightclubs, the once grand building's dark structures rub shoulders with the Square's garish neon posters. The juxtaposition of grandeur and throwaway enables a space in which DIY culture and artistic practice can flourish.

This exhibition, curated by Priya Sharma and Caroline Smith, will showcase the artists' varying concepts and reactions to such a unique environment. They explore being touched by both the walls of the places and environments we inhabit, as well as the walls and structures we create within our awareness in relation to others' feelings and communication.

Courtesy Wolstenholme Creative Space

PHASE FIVE

34–36 Seel Street, L1 4AZ
21 September–27 November

PHASE FIVE is located in an old bank that was being converted into a nightclub before it went out of business during the conversion process. Three floors will host seven artists at the forefront of experimentation with new technologies.

Phil Jeck's *Pool of Voices* takes old records and turntables salvaged from junk shops, playing them as musical instruments. The combination of spoken word and synthetic sounds are music compositions in their own right.

Joe Diebes' *Scherzo* is a music film that explores the limits of human virtuosity, the convergence of human and machine. The virtuoso's desire to achieve machine-like speed and perfection is realised in exhilarating and disturbing dimensions. His performance fragments and recombines into an impossibly extended musical climax.

OpusXX by Miguel Angel Rios is a film with a very careful *mise-en-scène* and dense physical presence. It can be considered a requiem to the violence of our times but subtly hints at recent sites of acts of terrorism in the West; New York, Madrid and London.

Clemencia Echeverri, in her video project *Voz*, works with the sounds that exist within prisons. The artist evokes the idea of voices as the inner core of the body, the prisoners being detached from their external voice. This is the internal sense of identity of the forgotten people inside the building.

Percussion group SDH (Mayke Nas and Wouter Snoei) use sound-enhanced blackboards to create a meeting point between music and image. In *I Delayed People's Rights by Walking Slowly in Narrow Hallways*, the audience completes the collaboration, resulting in a new musical composition.

Composer and performer Ray Lee has created a site-specific sound installation that explores the invisible phenomena of the PHASE FIVE space.

In Juan Cruz's *Repairs*, fragments of writing from unfinished or aborted attempts to write poems, stories, plays and novels are deployed in relation to simple wooden boxes that serve as seats from which to read the texts and supports on which to pin them. The boxes also have the potential to call to mind the implicit sound of the text.

Play by Giuseppe Stampone consists of five custom-made sound installation coffins inspired by countries that have played an important role in the collapse of the world economy.

'Music is one of the ways the soul gets to heaven'

Torquato Tasso

Image courtesy of Guiseppe Stampone

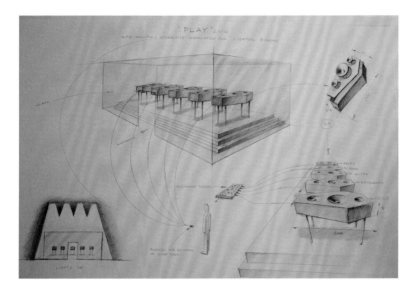

By Ours by Imogen Sidworthy focuses on residential demolition in Liverpool. The restructuring of language that accompanies physical and social change echoes the sound of demolition – one of the concrete expressions of economic inequality in which coherent structures are tumbled into the bleakness of urban upheaval.

Beatbox by Jani Ruscica video portrays sound and movements as self-expressive navigational tools. In the style of the cities symphonies, the beatboxers have created the entire soundtrack of the film by interpreting and imitating the sounds of their surroundings. The piece depicts an urban metropolis navigated by hip-hop artists.

BINARY CELL

40 Seel Street, L1 4BE
21–27 November
Opens: Tuesday–Saturday 14.00–18.00

In 2007 Stefan Kazassoglou (a musician, producer and computer whiz) and Graham Clarke (a Liverpool entrepreneur) acquired a lease on this derelict four-storey building in Seel Street. Over three years they transformed it into a multimedia hub called Binary Cell comprised of music studios (including a 5.1 surround mixing and mastering room), green screen film studios and resources for film production and events delivery.

To officially launch the building, No Longer Empty presents *Never Records* on the ground floor. *Never Records* is an installation by New York artist Ted Riederer, and resembles a functioning record store. Riederer has shown the work previously in Tower Records in New York but for SQUAT Liverpool 2010 he will be recording Liverpool bands and recording artists and creating, in an extension of his work in New York, a fake record label for them (Never Records) with fake posters and fake vinyl covers all created by him as if those groups were famous. The installation explores the line between what is real and what is fictional.

Frances Ewe: The Last Supper

102 Seel Street, L1 4BL
(viewable through window at street level)

In 2008 Frances Ewe staged a re-enactment of Da Vinci's *The Last Supper* using members of The Art Organisation. Ewe spent three days over Easter staging the photograph, leading up to the final click of a large-format camera by photographers Mccoy Wynne.

For SQUAT Liverpool 2010 Ewe will be presenting the photograph on the ground floor of 102 Seel Street which, for the last few years, has been acting as the accommodation base for artists visiting and participating in TAO projects. With the aid of a heritage grant secured by building owners Frensons Ltd in 2009, much of this building has been restored to its original glory and the house will continue to host visiting artists throughout the Biennial. It will also play host to a series of 'Super Socials', artists' dinners that encourage debate and networking over home-cooked food.

The photograph will be viewable from street level.

The video made of the photo shoot by Sam Meech will also be available to view by appointment from The International Gallery at 34 Slater Street, L1 4BX.

Courtesy of Ted Riederer

The International Gallery

34 Slater Street, L1 4BX

(space between)

18 September–2 October

High Tide is an interdisciplinary artist-led initiative which nurtures a creative culture of sustainability and ecological consideration of our lives. Their contribution to SQUAT Liverpool 2010 explores the ambiguous and intangible relationship that we have with the natural world.

www.hightideuk.org

New Emerging Artist

7–23 October

Kirsty E. Smith makes sculptural works in response to her surroundings, the domestic in particular. Her intention is to create work which resonates on a deeply emotive level and which acts as a vehicle to reconnect with a 'place' or memory deep in our subconscious. She experiments with a vast array of materials; juxtaposing the ordinary and luxurious, the cheap and expensive, the reclaimed and recycled. These surreal sculptural forms are vessels which hold and suggest many ideas simultaneously and it is quite possible to believe that Smith's sculptures have an unseen life of their own.

Artumentory...!

28 October–28 November

TAO present *Artumentary...!*, a compilation exhibition of new works selected from an open call that was spread through artists' networks and various groups/studios run by TAO in London, Liverpool and Nottingham. The artists have been asked not only to respond to the issues of empty spaces being revitalised and reappropriated through the creative process but also to look to the future possibilities of TAO as an organisation. The exhibition will attempt to outline a new blueprint for working in cities and in the private/public space.

Courtesy of Gregory Scott-Gurner

Casa de Brujes
The Old Big Issue Building

124 Duke Street, L1 5AG
19 September–29 November

The Constant Garden

During Mariela Bocanegra's time living in Parisian art squats, she was struck by the practice of locking up many of the city-centre parks at night. These are useful spaces, as much in the night as in the day. Guards patrol every evening: blowing whistles, get out, they are saying, the public has now become private.

For *The Constant Garden* Bocanegra works with a group of artists including Parabhen Lad to create one of these public/private gardens. By day the public will be able to bring their packed lunches and relax in this new space. They are encouraged to contribute to and work on the garden, helping it grow. By night, contrary to the gardens in Paris, you are encouraged to return, roam and discover who else is sharing your nocturnal adventure.

John Pountain: l'heure esquise

l'heure esquise (the exquisite hour) is a new series of pastels and drawings by Pountain based on an installation *the sitting room* shown earlier this year at Casa de Brujes. The installation replicated Vermeer's studio, inviting people to sit and have their portraits drawn. The results were deeply atmospheric, seemingly of Vermeer's time but creating new narratives between the invoked artist (Vermeer), the living artist (Pountain) and the visitor/subject.

Elizabeth Willow

Elizabeth Willow's work weaves natural and mythical ideas to create intricate sculptures, performances, poetry and installation. Using processes such as flower-arranging, embroidery and taxidermy she will create a new work for the Brujes.

Nicholas Williams: Dark Paintings

Williams will be showing a new collection of paintings made during the recent move of studio group Casa de Brujes to their new, as yet un-electrified building on Duke Street. Made mostly at night in a studio lit by one battery light and some candles, Williams's normally vibrant folk-sci-fi paintings become muted and more sombre in tone, the flags of a future gone wrong.

East Village Arts Fair

Duke Street
18 September–27 September

Acting as a conduit between the artist and the public, East Village Arts (EVA) is a weekly arts and crafts fair located on Duke Street. The fair will be run every Saturday for duration of the Biennial. EVA supports local and regional creative practitioners by providing an environment for weekend trade. The fair will also be supported by micro stalls serving gourmet cuisine.

Courtesy Nicholas Williams

Octopi

81 Renshaw Street, L1 2SJ
17 September–27 November
Open: Monday–Saturday 10.30–18.00(ish)

Octopi is much more than just a shop: it is a meeting place for artists and the public to engage in a conversation. A viewing platform, to look inward and outward at a changing city.

Founded in 2009, Octopi aims to raise awareness of a growing local creative community by facilitating a common market place, finding a middle ground between public, private, business and charity. Octopi is a space where community growth and local prosperity take priority. The space offers artists the opportunity to explore and professionalise their work within the context of a product. We, as artists, wish to provide a sustainable way of achieving a natural balance between commerce and culture.

Cheeky Sew and Sew

79 Renshaw Street, L1 2SJ
17 September–27 November
Project viewable from window.

Cheeky Sew and Sew is a small bespoke costume service run by Frances Heap and Maria Luisa Olmos. With the help of TAO the space is transformed into a living/working gallery which will allow the public to peer in and see the entire costume-making process, from designing and pattern cutting to the fitting and finishing of an original garment.

Collaborating with companies such as TILT and Movema as well as supporting local businesses such as the local club the Kazimier, Cheeky Sew and Sew use recycled clothes and hold workshops to teach others how to make alterations and construct costumes with basic sewing skills. They provide a friendly community hub for people working in similar fields, creating a space in which they can communicate, share ideas, conduct workshops and share their expertise.

Courtesy of Gregory Scott-Gurner

Marina Rosenfeld – P.A.

Renshaw Hall, Benson Street, L1 2ST
17 September–27 November
Open: 12.00–17.00

Borrowing its form from the 'public
address' systems of social gathering
places, Marina Rosenfeld's P.A. will use
the complex overhead airspace and daily
function of Liverpool's historic Renshaw
Hall, now a car park, as both a reflecting
and distorting structure for sound.
Visitors to the site will encounter several
oversized loudspeakers installed overhead,
sweeping the architecture and transient
residents of the space – both human
and vehicular – with the artist's musical
deployment of fragments of speech and
pre-recorded sound.

EVEN

63 Renshaw Street, L1 2SJ
17 September–27 November
Open:

EVEN's work explores derelict spaces
in Liverpool and Japan. Between June
and August, EVEN participated in an
exhibition in the Noto Prefecture, Japan,
creating a series of new artworks made
from discarded material he found in this
rural Japanese location. Following this
exhibition he hitch-hiked to Tokyo to live
among homeless communities, creating
new work and street art centred around
the question 'What is Wealth'. EVEN is
interested in engaging with the world
outside of money in order to live freely.

Bringing this experience (and some of the
objects made there) back to Liverpool in
September, EVEN examines the creative
lives of those on or below the breadline
in both rural Japan and urban Liverpool.
Before the artist embarked on his voyage
to Japan he said: 'In London and Liverpool
it is easy to find food, materials, tools,
paints and surfaces for free and I feel like
the experience of finding it there (Japan)
will influence my work considerably.'

EVEN will transform the Renshaw
Street space based on the houses of the
Japanese homeless, using it to house
sound installations and photography and
incorporating elements of the artist's
work made in both Japan and Liverpool
alongside site-specific wall painting made
especially for the exhibition.

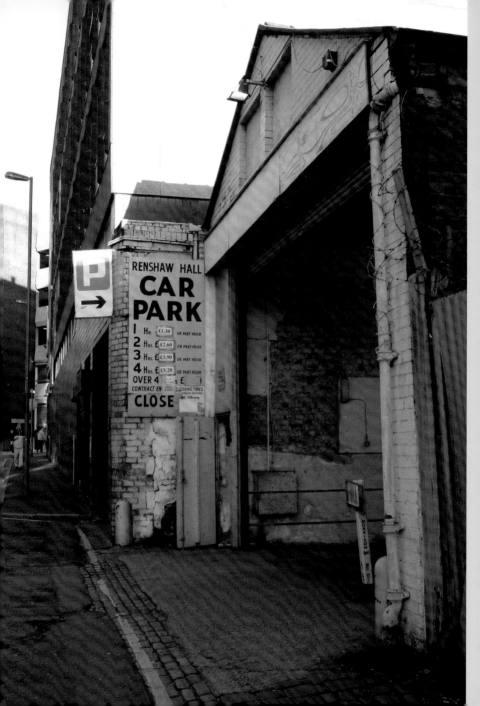

Judy Chicago: *Song of Songs*
The Black-E

1 Great George Street, L1 5EW
+44 (0)151 709 5109   www.theblack-e.co.uk
All works courtesy of Joe Cain

15

For over four decades, as a renowned artist, writer, feminist and intellectual, in the USA and internationally, Judy Chicago's influence has been far-reaching within and outside the art community. She has made the female point of view a part of mainstream art.

In 1982 Chicago was guest speaker for *Sister to Shakespeare*, the Black-E's tribute to Virginia Woolf on the centenary of her birth, when she delivered a lecture on *Women, Art and Society*, conceived as a sequel to Woolf's lecture of the same title. Her visit included seminars both at the Black-E and Liverpool College of Art.

Today the Black-E presents Chicago's *Song of Songs*, a series of twelve paired prints, created by Chicago from 1997–99. This evocative series, inspired by Marcia Falk's new translation of the biblical text, uses an innovative combination of lithography and helio-relief (a photomechanical process for creating a wood block) to explore mutuality of desire and a shared enjoyment of sexual pleasure that is unusual in the history of art. *Song of Songs* has only been exhibited once before in the UK (at the Fitzwilliam Museum, Cambridge) and is loaned to the Black-E by Bill Harpe.

Chicago has remained steadfast in her commitment to the power of art as a vehicle for intellectual transformation and social change. She was a major contributor to the Feminist Art movement in the 1970s, and remains one of its best-known proponents. She often uses 'womanly' crafts like needlework and painted china to create images of lasting strength and pride in women's accomplishments. Equally important to her is the creation of objects that will last for generations, so that future women will understand what came before.

Chicago is the author of eight books, including *Through the Flower: My Struggle as a Woman Artist*, *The Dinner Party: A Symbol of Our Heritage* and *Women and Art: Contested Territory* with Edward Lucie-Smith.

HER VOICE

Yes I am black and radiant...

Will you disrobe me with your stares?

The eyes of many morning suns
Have pierced my skin and now I shine
Black as the light before the dawn.

HIS VOICE

Until
the day is over,
shadows gone,

I'll go
up to the hills
of fragrant bloom

How fine
you are, my love,
my perfect one

Tony Cragg: Sculpture
The Well, Liverpool Cathedral

Liverpool Cathedral
1 St James' Mount, L1 7AZ
Open: daily 8.00–18.00

This presentation of Tony Cragg's sculpture, a selection made for the Well of Liverpool Cathedral, represents a kind of home-coming for the artist, who was born in Liverpool, and for whom the Cathedral was an imposing (and unfinished) sculptural presence during his childhood. It's hard to imagine a more challenging material environment for a sculptor's work to inhabit.

Cragg has never allowed his work to become characterised by a single stylistic signature in form, method or material, although these three sculptures are in fact each generated in the same way – through the repetition of the circle to form a skin containing a volume. For Cragg, energy is an article of faith. Everything in his environment is a material to be shaped, and the dialogue with each material is made visible through form.

'Very few kilograms of sculpture are made on an average day while many billions of tons of materials are made into other more "useful" things' the artist comments in 'To Viersen Sculpture', 1996. 'Sculpture ... is an attempt to make dumb material express human thoughts and emotions. It is the attempt not just to project intelligence into material, but also, to use material to think with. Sculptures at their best are not just the result of an artist taking a material ... and forcing it into a form ... but ... the material finds itself in a new form and the sculptor finds himself with new content and new meaning. There are many refinements that one can make to this description of the sculptural process, but basically, the sculptor engages the material with what he knows and comes away knowing more.'

Although Cragg has worked in most of the materials available to a sculptor, those chosen for this show set the artworks apart from the stone structure and surfaces of the Well, while nonetheless making a connection – suggesting the Cathedral is an instrument for thinking just as much as are the sculptures.

Big Head, 2000
Fibreglass, 260 x 148 x 142 cm

Also showing
Wooden Crystal, 2000
Wood, 407 x 108 x 108 cm

I'm Alive, 2003
Carbon, kevlar, 240 x 245 x 390 cm

LIVERPOOL CATHEDRAL

Earth and Aether, 2010
Lin Holland and Jane Poulton

The Chapter House, Liverpool Cathedral
1 St James' Mount, L1 7AZ
Open: daily 8.00–18.00

Earth and Aether is an artwork designed specifically for the Chapter House of Liverpool Cathedral by artists-in-residence Lin Holland and Jane Poulton.

In the centre of the tiled floor is a large piece of red sandstone that has been covered in hand-beaten gold leaf. Directly above it, apparently hovering in mid-air, is a mirrored 'house'.

Through its use of materials and forms – chosen for their physical, aesthetic and symbolic relevance in a religious setting – the artwork evokes humanity's attempt, through the sanctification of earthly objects, to approach a sense of the sublime.

Earth and Aether explores a variety of themes, including 'reality' and faith, permanence and transformation, here and hereafter.

Lin Holland and Jane Poulton
Earth and Aether (preparatory drawing)
Red sandstone, gold, mirror
90 x 70 cm with height variable

LIVERPOOL CATHEDRAL

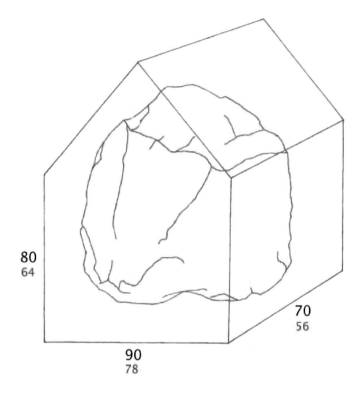

80
64

70
56

90
78

Liverpool School of Art and Design MA Fine Art Exhibition

Liverpool John Moores University
Duckinfield Street, L3 5RD
www.ljmu.ac.uk/lsa
Open: Monday–Friday 12.00–18.00

The MA was established during Liverpool's year as European Capital of Culture in 2008 to contribute towards a legacy of ongoing cultural renewal in the city. The programme was devised in collaboration with Liverpool Biennial, Tate Liverpool and FACT, and has drawn on advice and expertise from many other arts organisations in Liverpool including the Bluecoat, Static and Ceri Hand Gallery. This will be the first MA show presented by LJMU.

The programme provides an opportunity for a small group of students to develop their practice in relation to a global context that is filtered through the rich artistic infrastructure of Liverpool. Lectures, seminars and tutorials take place in the Art and Design Academy and are also hosted by some of our partner organisations. This enables students to benefit from the academic debate generated in the university together with the practical input and critical discussion that takes place when their work and ideas are put into direct contact with a network of live and internationally networked professional environments. The final exhibition, which locates the work of graduating students within the context of an International Biennial, is testament to that engagement.

This first group of students have helped us to shape the programme by doing what artists should and confounding our expectations – reminding us that, for all the things we might conveniently want art to be, it is by delivering that which we don't expect and which we cannot necessarily rationalise or understand that art becomes really important.

Featured students; Clare Brumby, Andrea Cotton, Ben Egerton, Jane Fairhurst and Tim Fielding, Martin Hearne, Adam Gregory, David Hancock and Nicola Smith.

Nicola Smith
Departures

Jane Fairhurst and Tim Fielding
Untitled

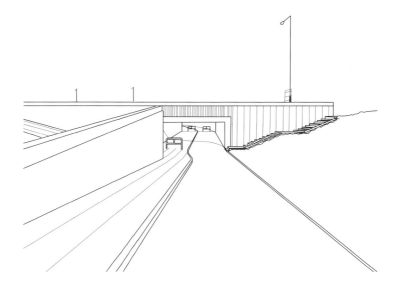

Astrid Kirchherr: A Retrospective
Victoria Gallery & Museum

University of Liverpool, Ashton Street, L69 3DR
25 August–29 January 2011
Open: Tuesday–Saturday 10.00–17.00
Admission free   www.liv.ac.uk/vgm

Astrid Kirchherr is best known for her photographs of the Beatles during the early Hamburg days and for her association with the Beatles' original bass player, Stuart Sutcliffe.

Kirchherr was the first person to take studio shots of the Beatles and her photographs capture the innocence and ambition of the Beatles as they took their formative steps to stardom. She later photographed the group when their fame had escalated and they had left Liverpool behind.

This exhibition is a rare opportunity to view a remarkable collection of photographs from a seminal moment in popular culture and in Liverpool's history. Images of war-damaged Liverpool provide a stark contrast to the buzz and excitement of the youth movement.

The curators were allowed unparalled access to Kirchherr's substantial archives. 70 images will be shown, from the early days when she first met the Beatles in Hamburg to her assignment to *A Hard Day's Night* in 1964 for *Stern* magazine which brought her back to Liverpool.

Metal

Edge Hill Railway Station, Tunnel Road, L7 6ND
0151 707 2277

Dream Machine
15 September–23 October

Metal is housed in Edge Hill Station, the oldest passenger railway station still in use and to mark the 180th anniversary of the opening of the Liverpool to Manchester railway they present *Dream Machine*. With artists from both Liverpool and Manchester this exhibition will celebrate and explore the first rail journey made between two cities, and the significance of this historic moment on modern life. Through a series of large-scale works that reflect on time, routine, direction and discipline – qualities that all inform the artistic process – the exhibition seeks to reflect the beat and rhythm of train travel. Influenced by the knowledge that railway timetabling or 'railway time' was in fact the catalyst for a standardised time system across the UK, the first time regional and London times met, the work will show how the train journey is an enduring source for artistic inspiration.

Dream Machine will feature Nicola Dale and composer Ailis Ni Riain, Phil Lockhart, Tom Palin and Richard Proffitt.

Future Station
16–20 November

The Future Station mini-festival in November has been in development over the past year and will feature finished work, work in progress and on-the-spot happenings from members of the group including; 'On the Edge', a documentation of life within small businesses on Wavertree Road by Jane Hughes; film screenings from local artists Paul Fred Kelly and Mark Tierney; a sculpture in progress from artist Adrian Jeans; and The Suitcase Ensemble performing, developing and holding workshops for a new piece of music theatre, plus many more. Please check the website for further details.

The Future Station group is an open network of individuals who meet every month at the station to develop ideas for the spaces, work with Metal's artists-in-residence, and to create and encourage collaboration between the group. Metal have been based in the area for five years working with local residents, schools, individuals and organisations to excavate personal testimonies and imaginative responses to the local area. In October 2009 they renovated the former station buildings at Edge Hill to become a space for local people and artists from all disciplines to come together, to create new work and to share ideas.

Nicola Dale and Ailis Ni Riaian
DOWN

THE
ROYAL
STANDARD

Unit 3, Vauxhall Business Centre, 131 Vauxhall Road, L3 6BN
0151 236 1919   www.the-royal-standard.com
Open: Wednesday–Sunday 11.00–18.00   Fully accessible

Hierarchies of Allegiance

Christian Newby, Jonathan Baldock, Pil &
Galia Kollectiv
17 September–17 October
Preview 16 September, 17.00–21.00,
(including a performance by Pil & Galia Kollectiv)

Hierarchies of Allegiance brings
together a group of artists whose work
encompasses film, performance, drawing
and installation. Linked as much by
the artists' interests in examining art
historical figures as by their sensitivity to
myth, custom and symbolism, the works
in *Hierarchies of Allegiance* share a rich
aesthetic that references the uncanny, the
darkly humorous and the melancholic.

Each artist strongly identifies and engages
with particular socio-cultural subjects,
reconfiguring these in unique ways to
parody social traditions and meditate
on the relationships between the occult,
modernist theatre and arcane ritual.

DEADPAN

David Sherry, Jamie Shovlin, Jess Flood-
Paddock, Jock Mooney, Josephine Flynn,
Laura Ford, Laurina Paperina, Miles
Thurlow, Noel Clueit, Toby Huddlestone
29 October–28 November
Preview 28 October, 17.00–21.00
(including a performance by David Sherry)

With a good glug of irony and a sarcastic
nod, *DEADPAN* gives a kick up the arse
to the utter mess of an art world at a
point of oversaturation by questioning
the strategies used by artists to make
new work. Considering mimicry and
the referential alongside the blatancy
of homage, *DEADPAN* presents with
barefaced cheek a *pastiched* viewpoint
of art with lampooning consequences,
providing a glimpse into the dirty world of
satire within contemporary art today.

Jock Mooney
St Francis Is a Sissy, 2007
Plastic modelling compound, enamel paint

Ceri Hand Gallery

12 Cotton Street, L3 7DY
Open: Wednesday–Saturday 10.00–18.00
0151 207 0899   www.cerihand.co.uk

Nick Crowe and Ian Rawlinson
No Sign of Helicopters
16 September–16 October

For their debut exhibition at the Ceri Hand Gallery, Crowe and Rawlinson present a new body of work exploring issues of containment and release.

The Hunters, a group of twelve coils of rope hung on a line of wall brackets, sets the tone for the show. Suggestive of a group of disciples, the kit room of a mountain rescue team or local lynch mob, it's a darkly foreboding work.

Crowe and Rawlinson will also premiere a spectacular new work entitled *Die Brücke*, filmed at night during the dismantling of a railway bridge in Berlin.

No Sign of Helicopters sets up a series of poetic resonances between place, person and activities. While some works allude to spectacle and escape, there is an ever-present concern with the individual constrained and positioned by social forces. This is a world explored in partial glimpses. Vignettes of anxiety and release evoking images of labour, energy and heat are as much symptoms of the retreat into nostalgia as they are of what might once have been called purposeful industriousness.

Rebecca Lennon
We are stuck here together
28 October–28 November (Preview 27 October)

Rebecca Lennon's first solo show at Ceri Hand draws together the found, the stolen, the forged, the made and the remade in a series of exchanges and situations, nuanced with an often-ritualised, misplaced and convoluted drive to connect, act or validate.

Old photos bought by weight in markets and on eBay, art sent to a debt-collection agency as an offering for the debt, a film clip of a man acting out a sleep disorder, and a family member who swam across Morcambe Bay in exchange for a wooden chest of drawers, are brought together in a show eating its tail, perpetually shifting between the personal and the inauthentic, the humorous and something darker.

Nick Crowe & Ian Rawlinson
Study for 'Monument', 2010
Drum kit, 219 x 56 cm
Courtesy of the artists and Ceri Hand Gallery

Independents
LIVERPOOL BIENNIAL

As always, the Independents are an inspiring mix of internationally experienced artists as well as national and local young and mid-career artists. The range of work has no bounds and in 2008 included film, performance and installations as well as gallery exhibitions. Locations are diverse, from one-off street performances to more formal gallery exhibitions, and works shown in schools, bars, shops, online and at major locations. The Independents are not themed, categorised or curated by the city's institutions; they exist on their own terms, doing their own thing, looking for attention, dialogue and interaction.

Among the many events, you can see a solo show of new paintings by John Moores prize-winner Martin Greenland at Hope University, Italian photographers in Calderstones Park, Find a Pound in random places and The Stuckists at View Two. Dave White is inviting people to an exclusive viewing in his Liverpool studio of his new collection 'Forgotten Alchemy'. There will be studio group shows, edgy installations in unusual places, Jason Jones paintings in John Lewis's homeware department and an Arts & Craft show in the Metropolitan Cathedral.

There are sculpture and design shows at the Bluecoat Display Centre and more exhibitions at the Liverpool Academy of Arts, The Bridewell, Domino Gallery, LCAD, the Stanhope Street and Clayton Sqaure galleries, Blackburne House and the Gostins building, which includes the Arcade and Liver Sketching Club.

You can also contemplate the artworks while taking a break at various cafés and bars, including Egg, 33–45 Parr Street, Leaf Tea Rooms, Mocha Lounge, the Sandwich Bureau, the Quaker Meeting House café, Oomoo and the Quarter.

There are several events on Wirral including group shows at the new Six Rooms Gallery in Argyle Street featuring more than 25 artists, the Oxton art fair at the Williamson Gallery and the House of Fraser shop windows.

Full up-to-date listings are on the website: www.independentsbiennial.org

info@independentsbiennial.org

Courtesy Martin Greenland

Public Art in Liverpool

Liverpool's wealth of contemporary public artworks can be found in the city centre, in the suburbs and on the coast. You will find some just walking between Biennial exhibitions. Some need a detour and shouldn't be missed: if you have an afternoon to spare, see *Dream* at Sutton Manor; alternatively, at dusk, there's no better place to be than at *Another Place* on Crosby Beach watching the sun set behind the lonely army of iron men.

© Jaume Plensa,
St Helens Council,
Stuart Rayner 2009

Penelope. Jorge Pardo

WOLSTENHOLME SQUARE, L1 4JJ

It's not easy to design artwork for the street that's fun and fit for use. Located in Wolstenholme Square at the heart of clubland, by day Jorge Pardo's *Penelope* provides a colourful resting perch for seagulls. At night, it comes alive, the glowing bulbs an absurd backdrop to the mood and experience of both revellers and passers-by.

Roman Standard. Tracey Emin

THE ORATORY

If the Liver birds on the Liver Building come to life and fly away, the myth has it, Liverpool will sink. *Roman Standard* is Tracey Emin's riff on this local myth. Since 2008 a small bird has sat on a 4-metre-high pole at the gates of The Oratory (inside is Laura Belém's *Thousand Bells* commissioned for *Touched*), a blink and you miss it. When noticed, its subtlety is rewarding; but mostly it keeps to its perch, guarding, waiting and watching the world about it.

Emin's neon work, *For You* (2008), is also on view at the Anglican Cathedral right next door.

Dream. Jaume Plensa

SUTTON MANOR COLLIERY SITE
SUTTON WOODLAND, JUBITS LANE
ST HELENS, WA9 4BB
01744 755150
WWW.DREAMSTHELENS.COM

Visible from the M62, but well worth the walk up the hill, Jaume Plensa's *Dream* is a collaboration between the artist and a small group of local ex-miners who worked at the former Sutton Manor Colliery. The result is a dream for the future, a 20-metre-high girl's head in shimmering white gives the effect of a hologram as you approach, not quite real.

Liverpool to Liverpool. Simon Faithfull

LIME STREET STATION
LIME ST, L1 1JD
WWW.SIMONFAITHFULL.ORG

Liverpool to Liverpool, at the main entrance to the station, consists of drawings etched into the windows and paving stones underfoot. It is based on Faithfull's electronic 'field journal' drawings made in 2008 during his trip from Liverpool to Nova Scotia using buses, trains and a container ship. Simon Faithfull will also be giving a talk based on *Liverpool to Liverpool*. Go to page 220 for more information.

Turning the Place Over. Richard Wilson

CROSS KEYS HOUSE, MOORFIELDS
(OPPOSITE MOORFIELDS STATION)
TURNING THE PLACE OVER TURNS FROM SUNRISE
TO SUNSET
WWW.BIENNIAL.COM

Located at a former Yates Wine Lodge at Moorfields in Liverpool's city centre, *Turning the Place Over* is a brilliant feat in technical engineering. An 8-metre-diameter oval is cut from the façade of the building and revolves steadily in three dimensions powered by a specially designed giant rotator (the kind normally used in shipping and nuclear industries). One of Richard Wilson's few public interventions, the effect is startling and not to be missed.

Raleigh. Tony Cragg

ALBERT DOCK (GRASSY KNOLL NEAR PIERMASTERS
HOUSE), LIVERPOOL, L3 4AN

Raleigh was commissioned in 1986 during the conversion of a part of Albert Dock into Tate Liverpool, intended as a celebration for the opening in 1988. The title refers to the famous *The Boyhood of Raleigh*, 1870, by Sir John Everett Millais, presented to the Tate by Amy, Lady Tate, in memory of Sir Henry Tate in 1900. The sculpture is both a reminder of the origins of the Tate Gallery in Henry Tate's Liverpool, but also a personal tribute by Tony Cragg to the city of his childhood.

The sculpture is made of industrially cast elements – two twisted cast-iron horns resting on a plinth of rough granite – and the final form was not decided before the artwork's installation: the individual elements were craned into place and arranged according to how the pieces locked together *in situ*.

Tony Cragg is also showing at Liverpool Anglican Cathedral during the 2010 Liverpool Biennial. Go to page 190 for more information.

Another Place. Antony Gormley

MARINERS ROAD, CROSBY BEACH, SEFTON, L23 6SX
WWW.VISITSOUTHPORT.COM

This masterpiece by Antony Gormley is situated on Crosby Beach in Sefton. Consisting of 100 life-size figures spread along three kilometres of the beach and one kilometre out into the sea, the experience of the artwork is dependent on the tide and weather conditions. Crosby Beach is easily accessible from Liverpool city centre: take a 16-minute train ride from Liverpool Central or Moorfields, and get off at Waterloo.

Antony Gormley also has work on show in the collection at Tate Liverpool. Go to page 82 for Tate's visiting information.

Rotunda Pavilion. Gross Max

ROTUNDA
109 GREAT MERSEY STREET, L5 2PL

In 2007 and 2008 Rotunda College worked with internationally acclaimed landscape architects Gross Max to develop a patch of derelict land in front of their building. The result was a community garden split into two parts: a folly (with its own vertical garden) and mixed use 'barcode' environment with varying strips of land used for different community growing projects. The folly is still in use as a social hub for outdoor events and its combination of industrial material intertwined with greenery suggests the harmony possible when urban spaces are designed to interact with natural growth and forms.

Liverpool Biennial 2010 Visitor Centre

52 Renshaw Street, L1 4EN
Open: daily 10.00–18.00
Tel: 0845 220 2800   www.biennial.com
Free Entry   Fully Accessible

Liverpool Biennial has once again teamed up with Pollard Thomas Edwards architects, and are delighted to be working with John Lewis for the first time, to create a welcoming space inside the former Rapid Hardware shop on Renshaw Street.

Visitors will be able to access information about the Liverpool Biennial 2010 programme, purchase festival merchandise, check email with free wifi, buy tea, coffee and soft drinks and healthy snacks and relax in the urban forest – you are welcome to bring a picnic.

Exhibition tours are available for large groups, school visits or anyone interested in discovering more about Liverpool or the visual arts in general (for more information on tours and talks please see opposite page). There are plenty of places to relax, talk about the art and catch up with friends.

Staff and volunteers are on hand to help you get the most out of the six programmes within the festival as well as offering information to help you navigate the city. If you are unsure, just ask one of our volunteers.

Look out for regular events taking place within the Visitor Centre throughout Liverpool Biennial 2010 and make sure you get information to take away on all our events each week or add your own comments to our 'wall of words'.

Visitor Services Partner

John Lewis

Supported by

PTEa
Pollard Thomas Edwards

Touched Tours and Education

Daily tours 12.00–13.30
Free guided tour of the *Touched* exhibition by our Biennial invigilators. These tours will follow the particular interests of the individual and will cover different elements of the exhibition every day. Tours start at the Biennial Visitors Centre.

Every Saturday 15.30–17.00
Free guided tours of the *Touched* exhibition (focusing particularly on the 52 Renshaw Street building) by a variety of different art mediators. Tours start at the Biennial Visitors Centre.

Every Sunday 15.30–17.00
The Sunday tours focus on the public realm elements of *Touched*. They follow the same format as above (starting at the Biennial Visitors Centre).

Early Sundays 10.30–11.30
These tours will be led by poets, musicians, composers, artists and curators and many will take a more experimental approach to the format of an exhibition tour. Please see the events listing at the back of this guide to find out more information.

There is a maximum of 15 persons per tour – booking is required for all tours – please visit www.biennial.com, call 0845 220 2800 or email visit@biennial.com. Unless otherwise stated all tours will start from the Biennial Visitors Centre, 52 Renshaw Street, L1 4EN.

TATE LIVERPOOL

Wednesdays and Saturdays 14.00–15.00
These tours will focus on the Tate Liverpool presentation of *Touched*. Booking required. Tours cost £5. Meet at *Touched* exhibition entrance (fourth floor). Call +44 (0)151 702 7400 for more information see page 82 for venue details.

Tate Liverpool Learning Team organises a varied programme of activities and events at the Gallery, catering for all types of groups and individuals. Programmes can also be delivered in school and community settings across the city region. If you wish to experience *Touched* with our learning team contact us by email (visiting.liverpool@tate.org.uk) or by telephone +44 (0)151 702 7400.

Drawing with Sound, the Big Draw at Tate Liverpool (in the Studio)
23–31 OCTOBER
DROP IN 13.30–16.30
Ever wondered what music would look like if it were a drawing? Families are welcome to the Big Draw during half-term for this free event – experiment in drawing with sound, inspired by *Touched*.

THE BLUECOAT

Saturdays 14.00–14.45

Tours will run every Saturday focusing on the Bluecoat's presentation of the *Touched* exhibition. Tours are free but booking is required. Please call +44 (0)151 702 5324 for more information see page 104 for venue details.or email info@thebluecoat.org.uk. Group tours can also be booked in advance.

On Saturday 9 October, Bluecoat *Touched* curator Sara-Jayne Parsons will lead a tour taking an insightful and personal view of her chosen artists.

Explore at the Bluecoat

EVERY SATURDAY AND SUNDAY
DROP IN 12.00–16.00
Free, fun, creative, hands-on activities for all the family – all of the activities are designed to respond to *Touched*.

Schools explore at the Bluecoat

Schools explore at the Bluecoat offers a guided tour of *Touched* and space for teacher-led activities. Materials are available, themed around listening, exploring vocabulary, colours, numeracy and different ways of thinking. Work with our team in advance to plan how the exhibition and the building itself can become a resource for curriculum-related activities. There are also sessions available for secondary education.

Contact Laura Pilgrim at laura.pilgrim@thebluecoat.org.uk or +44 (0)151 702 7761 to find out more.

FACT

Free tours of the FACT presentation of the *Touched* exhibition are available by advance booking only from Monday – Saturday (10.00–16.30). Please discuss any specific needs when booking. Staff can also be booked to talk to your group in a classroom setting. Please contact Joan Burnett by emailing info@fact.co.uk or call +44 (0)151 707 4464. See page 118 for venue information.

A FOUNDATION

A Foundation run a bespoke tours service.

Information on events and workshops will be available on our website, www.afoundation.org.uk or contact Clare Warren by email info@afoundation.org.uk or telephone +44 (0)151 706 0600. See page 132 for venue information.

THE WALKER

Tours of the *John Moores Painting Prize* will run on 24 September, 8 October, 4 November and 7 December. All tours start at 13.00 and last for approximately 45 minutes. For further information and booking please go to www.liverpoolmuseums.org.uk or call +44 (0)151 4784697. See page 138 for venue information.

Touched audio guide

Artist's audio responses to *Touched* can be downloaded from www.biennial.com or can be picked up from the Biennial Visitor's Centre from 18 September.

Touched educator's pack

This free resource is specifically designed to support educators in the planning and delivery of a group visit to the *Touched* exhibition. The pack provides a valuable introduction to the theme, as well as a guide to the work on display at each venue. It includes suggestions for viewpoints and activities that can help to promote discussion, understanding and enjoyment of the work among students of all ages. The pack is available to download free at www.biennial.com from September 2010.

Young Mediators Programme

There is the opportunity for schools, colleges and university groups to work with our professional art mediators, curators and Liverpool Biennial staff team to learn about the *Touched* exhibition and develop tours and discourse projects.

Places are free but limited on this programme. Please contact samantha@biennial.com to discuss the programme further, check availability and make a booking.

Touched Film Programme:
The Artists Cinema

The Artists Cinema takes six recently-commissioned films, shot on 35mm by contemporary artists working with moving image, and injects them into the programme of general release feature films at FACT – reminiscent of 'shorts' in the now-obsolete cinematic double bill. In this playful format, The Artists Cinema examines the cultural context of artists' moving image by taking it from the gallery – imbued with a critical thinking approach, where audiences regularly drop in and out of the installation – to the cinema, where the suspension of belief is encouraged, entertainment is forefronted and emotional vulnerability is cultivated. This change of format brings with it a phenomenological enquiry, into what the subjective and material experience of moving image is in relation to the interpretation of its content.

Widening the reach of the Biennial, many in the audience will come across the films by chance in a usual night out at the theatre, creating a surprise or subversive dialogue between the films and the feature releases they are screened in front of. Shown in partnership with Lux and the Independent Cinema Office, The Artists' Cinema layers the cinematic experience on the growing field of contemporary moving image.

Entry to The Artists' Cinema films are granted with ticket purchase of feature films listed. All feature films subject to change. Check www.fact.co.uk to confirm dates and times.

17–23 September
Akram Zaatari – *Tomorrow Everything Will be Alright*

Screening with *Winter's Bone* (dir. Debra Granik)

This film depicts a late night online chat, in an unexpected format, between two men who haven't met since the turn of the millennium. Their exchange is the familiar conversation of old lovers, and leads to their reunion after ten years of separation. The film navigates against time with an unsettling use of communication, recording technologies and temporal gaps.

24–30 September
Rosalind Nashashibi – *This Quality*

Screening with *Cyrus* (dir. Jay & Mark Duplass)

This Quality is a film shot in downtown Cairo. It comprises two halves: the first shows a 30-something woman looking directly at the camera, and sometimes acknowledging the existence of others around her who we cannot see. She has beautiful face with eyes which seem to see internally rather than outwardly, they almost have the appearance of being painted on, suggesting the blindness of a mythological seer. The second half shows a series of parked cars covered with fabric. Each car suggests a sightless face, as the fabric stretched around the machine turns it into a face but also seems to hood the car so that it is conspicuously hidden, like a child covering his eyes.

8–14 October
Aurélien Froment – *Pulmo Marina*

Screening with *A Town Called Panic*
(dir. Stéphane Aubier & Vincent Patar)

Against a uniform background of purest
Yves Klein blue, a pale yellow jellyfish roils
and bristles like a fragment of living lace,
while a slightly officious voiceover narrates
its baroque but literally brainless anatomy,
its voracious cannibalism and its classical
forebears (in French, such a creature is a
méduse). The apparently depthless blue is,
the narrator says, the rear of an elliptical
tank at Monterey Bay Aquarium, in which
the jellyfish is held in constant stasis by
two opposing currents of seawater.

15 – 21 October
Deimantas Narkevicius – *Ausgetraumt*

Screening with *Animal Kingdom*
(dir. David Michôd)

A small group of young Lithuanian
boys who have just started a band, are
interspersed with shots of their wintertime
surroundings in Vilnius. Pop or rock music
has never been fully developed in Lithuania
as a means of self expression, and no one
Lithuanian pop musician has reached
international acclaim. Narkevicius films
these young idealists and their international
ambitions, asking them questions about
their vision of the future, their reflections
on the political situation and the generally
unsatisfying cultural environment.

29 October–4 November
Amar Kanwar – *A Love Story*

Screening with *The Arbour* (dir. Clio Barnard)

A Love Story is a miniature narrative in
four acts where time becomes fluid as the
image is distilled to its inner self. The film
lies at the fringe of the expanding Indian
city, a world of continuous migration and
therefore of continuous separations. It is
in this terrain of separation that *A Love
Story* is located. This film can also be seen
as an offering to mainstream cinema, a
space where we often lose ourselves in the
repetitive spectacle of grand love stories.

5–11 November
Keren Cytter – *The Coat*

Screening with *Another Year* (dir. Mike Leigh)

A dramatic love triangle develops between
two brothers obsessed with the game
of sudoku and a beautiful young woman
from east Germany. As the story unfolds
the viewer is entwined in the turbulent
romance between the woman and the
younger British brother, who for the
past seven years has visited her behind
his brother's back. This colorful tragedy
combines a wide range of effects and
devices to tell its story, flirting with the
cinematic dream, the idea of seduction
and the visual representation of happiness.

Supported by
**ARTS COUNCIL
ENGLAND**

Events

Touched Conference

LIVERPOOL JOHN MOORES UNIVERSITY, 2 DUCKINFIELD STREET, L3 5RD
11.00–17.00
FREE ADMISSION. RESERVATION IS RECOMMENDED THROUGH
WWW.BIENNIAL.COM OR 0845 220 2800

As the story of doubting Thomas tells us, touch is the mark of truth, the most intimate gesture and the greatest commitment. To touch or to be touched is the performance of truth, when incredulity is displaced and the world condenses into a moment of all enveloping realisation, changing everything. But let us not limit touch to the physical: to be touched arrives unexpectedly through every sense – including thought – locating our most intimate moments in space and time. How to live by these moments where strength and vulnerability conjoin in both their terror and beauty is what we would define as commitment – a commitment to oneself and to the world that is both personal and political.

The *Touched* Conference has invited the artists, curators and thinkers involved in the making of the exhibition to discuss these three important aspects of *Touched*.

11.00–12.30
Performing Truths

PANEL PARTICIPANTS: Tehching Hsieh, artist; Alphonso Lingis, philosopher and Professor of Philosophy Emeritus of Penn State University; Coco Fusco, artist, writer and Chair of the Fine Art Department at Parsons/The New School for Design;
Tania Bruguera, artist.
Moderated by Mark Waugh, Director of A foundation Liverpool and Co-director of the International Curators Forum (ICF).

13.30–15.00
Between the Senses

PANEL PARTICIPANTS: Steven Connor, writer, critic, broadcaster and Professor of Modern Literature and Theory, Birkbeck College, London; Tony Chakar, artist, architect and writer; Jamie Isenstein, artist; Danica Dakić, artist.
Moderated by Peter Gorschlüter, former Head of Exhibitions and Displays Tate Liverpool, now Deputy Director of the Museum of Modern Art Frankfurt.

15.30–17.00
The Beauty of Commitment

PANEL PARTICIPANTS: Minerva Cuevas, artist; FREEE, artists; Alfredo Jaar, artist; Will Kwan, artist.
Moderated by Lorenzo Fusi, Curator Liverpool Biennial.

Akram Zaatari
*Tomorrow Everything
Will be Alright*

Short film screening with
Winter's Bone
(dir. Debra Granik)

FACT, 88 WOOD STRRET,
L1 4DQ
17–23 SEPTEMBER

See also page 214.

www.fact.co.uk for
screening times and prices.

Thierry Geoffroy
Critical Run 1: Can Art Touch a City?

18 SEPTEMBER
LJMU, 2 DUCKINFIELD STREET, L3 5RD
17.30
SEE ALSO 19 SEPTEMBER

Critical Running is a debating format conceived by the Danish French artist Thierry Geoffroy (also known for his Emergency Room at P.S.1/MOMA). In a collapsing world (he suggests) we cannot continue to sit and sleep through conferences or make small talk at openings. New forms of critical debate have to be activated. Running through the city, participants can train their awareness muscles on a journey that will leave them breathless but invigorated. Critical Runs have taken place all over the world: Moscow, Naples, Cairo, Brussels, Rotterdam, Barcelona, Venice, Lyon, New York, London, Istanbul, Athens, Paris, Hanoi, Siberia, Copenhagen, Stockholm.

Run, before it's too late!....

Each run will last for approximately 25 minutes and will be at an easy running level and speed. Please be aware that each run will be filmed.

Join the debate online www.emergency rooms.org/criticalrun.html

Brian Catling
Cyclops

FREE, LIMITED CAPACITY
THE BLUECOAT, SCHOOL LANE,
L1 3BX
13.00–19.00

Brian Catling will respond to
the *Touched* theme by testing
the boundary between curiosity
and repulsion through the
manifestation of his performance
persona Cyclops. Invited to
overcome the uncertainties of
interacting with this one- eyed
spectre, audiences may observe
the Cyclops roaming the streets
of Liverpool pursued by the
paparazzi, or peer from the
balcony into his zoo-like enclosure
at the Bluecoat.

Artist, filmmaker, poet and
academic, Catling's work oscillates
between monumental symbolism
and jet-black humour.

Early Sundays
Cathy
Butterworth

BIENNIAL VISITOR CENTRE,
52 RENSHAW STREET, L1 4EN
(STARTING POINT)
10.30–11.30

Performance artist Cathy
Butterworth leads an intriguing
exhibition tour as she responds
to the theme and artworks of
Touched.

For booking see page 211.

Thierry Geoffroy

Critical Run 2:
Is It Okay to Use Artists as
Vacuum Cleaners?

BIENNIAL VISITOR CENTRE,
52 RENSHAW STREET, L1 4EN
11.00

See page 217.

Brian Catling
Cyclops

FREE, LIMITED CAPACITY
THE BLUECOAT, SCHOOL LANE,
L1 3BX
13.00–18.00

Lying-down-on-the-ground

**A performance event devised and directed by
artist Sonia Khurana**

LIME STREET STATION, L1
13.00–16.00

Staged on the 'sidelines' of the larger art event, Khurana proposes
to insert a provocation, by playfully inviting passers-by to lie down
on the ground. The bodies lying thus are continually documented,
described or circumscribed.

Imasge courtesy of the artist

*'Beginning literally with affecting a change in the
participant's visual perspective, this simple act of lying
down soon begins to resonate with multiple layers of
oblique suggestions that are to do with dismantling the
norms of protected life, ranging from resistance, friction,
contamination, dispossession, to the absurd and the
allegorical. Autographical traces drawn on the ground
transform a singular act into a collective utterance.'*

Lying-down... aims to work on various registers across diverse
contexts and audiences. By employing a fairly simple, essential
and non-threatening form of social interaction, Khurana has been
able to draw large numbers of audiences to participate in this act of
lying down. This ongoing, public performative event continues to
take place across various cities, the most recent being Nagoya, as
part of the Aichi Triennale, and earlier in the summer a workshop
derived from this project took place at New Art Exchange in
Nottingham.

This act will culminate in a live performance event on the Long
Night, 18 November 2010 at the Walker Art Gallery, 18.00 to 22.00.

To participate please visit www.nae.org.uk/lyingdown.php,
www.biennial.com or www.liverpoolmuseums.org.uk/walker/

Presented by New Art Exchange and Nottingham Trent University
in association with The Walker (National Museums Liverpool).

Liverpool-to-Liverpool: Chronicles of an Aimless Journey
A performative lecture by Simon Faithfull

SEFTON SUITE, ADELPHI HOTEL,
RANELAGH PLACE, L3 5UL
15.00
FREE ADMISSION, NO BOOKING REQUIRED

This illustrated lecture tells the story of an absurd and epic journey by the artist from the Old World to the New. Travelling by container ship, train and bus, the lecture describes the dislocation of one person along the historic paths of trade and exodus across the Atlantic. Telling tales of migration, seafaring and a strange mirroring of locations, Faithfull uses the 181 drawings he made on this journey, as well as video and diary extracts, to illustrate the rambling narrative. The lecture is presented in the grand Sefton Suite of the Adelphi Hotel, itself a replica of the first-class smoking lounge on the ill-fated *Titanic* – a doppelganger of a room that now lies 2.5 miles beneath the surface of the Atlantic Ocean.

Presented by Whitstable Biennale in association with ArtSway.

For details of Simon Faithfull's permanent public artwork Liverpool-to-Liverpool at Lime Street Station go to page 208.

www.whitstablebiennale.com

Ai Weiwei
Fairytale
FACT, 88 WOOD STRRET, L1 4DQ
18.30
£4/£3 (MEMBERS AND CONCESSIONS)

Fairytale is a documentary that follows the ambitious artwork that Chinese artist Ai Weiwei created in the German town of Kassel for the exhibition *documenta 12*. It follows the artist as he flies 1001 of his fellow Chinese citizens into the town to act as both tourists – free to spend their time as they like – and participants in the artwork. Documenting the elaborate artwork from concept to completion, the documentary offers viewers an insight into Ai Weiwei's artistic working method, as well as revealing the complicated administrative process of organising 1001 passports, visas, travel plans and accommodation within the large and complex bureaucracy of China. The backdrop of this documentary is the lives and hopes of the individual participants, who are asked throughout to answer 99 questions, such as 'Can art change the world?' or 'What is a fairytale?' Through their answers they reveal much about the state of contemporary China and the living conditions which they hope to leave behind, if only temporarily, as tourists.

*Liverpool-to-Liverpool:
Chronicles of an Aimless
Journey
Simon Faithfull*

TOUCHED TALK
Touched talks is a series of lectures and conversations in which prominent artists and thinkers speak to the theme of Liverpool Biennial's *International 2010: Touched*. Previous talks by Steven Connor, Alfonso Lingis, Coco Fusco and Tony Chakar can be accessed on www.vimeo.com/biennial

Zia Sardar
Touched by Wonder: Art and Religion in the 21st Century
BIENNIAL VISITOR CENTRE, 52 RENSHAW STREET, L1 4EN
18.30
FREE ADMISSION. RESERVATION IS RECOMMENDED THROUGH
WWW.BIENNIAL.COM OR 0845 220 2800

Wonder is a uniquely human characteristic. It can express our best endeavours or take a turn for the worst. Religion and art have been vehicles for the expression of cultural achievement since the dawn of time, and both can generate wonder and awe within us. In mutual embrace they have created and shaped the public space. This talk considers how these entwined aspects of culture have lost touch with each other, creating separate audiences who contest the public space and have lost touch with shared understanding. It considers how the legacy of secularism and imperialism continue to deform the public space, fracturing and fragmenting audiences, and impoverishing social discourse by losing touch with the mutual embrace of religion and art as representations of wonder.

Ziauddin Sardar is a writer, broadcaster and cultural critic. His numerous books include *Postmodernism and the Other* and *Balti Britain: A Provocative Journey Through Asian Britain*. A Visiting Professor of Postcolonial Studies at the School of Arts, the City University, he is a former co-editor of *Third Text*. www. ziauddinsardar.com

Rosalind Nashashibi
This Quality

Short film screening with *Cyrus* (dir. Jay and Mark Duplass)

FACT, 88 WOOD STRRET, L1 4DQ
24–30 SEPTEMBER

See also page 214.

www.fact.co.uk for screening times and prices.

The Spider Project presents the premiere of
Time is what keeps the light from reaching us

THE BLUECOAT, SCHOOL LANE, L1 3BX
20.00
FREE ADMISSION (TICKETS FROM THE BLUECOAT RECEPTION)

An anarchic, multimedia puppetry performance based on the Grimm
brothers' *Hansel and Gretel*. Interpreting the story as a fable about
our dependence on economic and hierarchical structures, artists Gernot
Wieland (Austria), David Jacques (UK) and Carla Ahlander (Sweden)
collaborate with the Spider Project to interweave personal stories with the
infamous fairy tale.

The performance was developed with a view to examining certain political
and socio-economic concerns relating to the city of Liverpool. The
participants enact a performance devised by themselves in the manner of
a traditional puppet theatre show, the narrative being interwoven between
the voices of the characters (puppets), the puppeteers and the banter
staged with our invited audience.

Ultimately, our collaboration with the socio-culturally engaged work of the
Spider Project – addressing its creative writing class and theatre group –
offers an opportunity to explore issues related to hierarchy, gender, and
cultural identity. The story could at turns be imaginary, possibly splicing
fictitious and factual elements. It could be not only a psychological drama
but also a personal rendition of the city's history as realised through the
thoughts and beliefs of the performers themselves.

The Spider Project is a Liverpool-based social programme that produces
collaborative projects bringing together their participant group and
established practitioners in the visual arts, drama and literature.

Courtesy Galerie Andreas Huber

Courtesy Gernot Wieland

Exhibition Tour: John Moores Painting Prize 2010

THE WALKER,
WILLIAM BROWN STREET,
L3 8EL
13.00–13.45

First held in 1957, the John Moores Painting Prize is the UK's best-known painting competition. Part of Liverpool Biennial, the competition culminates in an exhibition held at the Walker every two years. Join us for a tour of this year's exciting entries and discover more about the judging process, artists and artworks.

This tour will also be held on the following dates: 8 October, 4 November, 7 December.

Antti Laitinen *performance*

A FOUNDATION, 67 GREENLAND STREET, L1 0BY
12.00
FREE ADMISSION

Artist Antti Laitinen invites the public to join him for a launching party to witness the first and possibly final voyage of the vessel he has made in Liverpool from ancient bark collected from the forest floor in Finland. The vessel will be transported from A Foundation to the Canoe Club at 110 Mariners Wharf, Queens Dock, L3 4DG. There it will be launched on the high tide and will endeavour to navigate the River Mersey.

Cry Me a River
A solo-climate-summit by Anna Mendelssohn

INTERNATIONAL GALLERY, 34 SLATER STREET, L1 4BX
25–27 SEPTEMBER
SEE WWW.THEARTORGANISATION.CO.UK FOR DETAILS

Everything is so much more complicated than you think. There are a million little strings attached to every choice you make. At some point I began to cry. And that went on for many months. Because how do you refreeze the ice up there? It just can't be done.

Seated at a conference table, a woman talks about the melting of glaciers and the polar ice caps. She cries. Her monologue is constructed from a variety of public statements on climate change, woven together to form a single, shifting and self-disintegrating polyphonic text-montage. Featured talking heads range from politicians, scientists, activists, surgeons, poets, city planners, deep ecologists, architects, through to a surplus-energy club owner. This discourse of multiple voices is occasionally interspersed with the performer's reflections on her own personal life. As the topic comes with many feelings, such as anger, hope and despair, these emotions are, whenever necessary, chemically reproduced and bio-engineered. *Cry Me A River* walks the thin ice between sense and senselessness, inner and outer worlds, the personal and the political.

Cry Me a River
Anna Mendelssohn

EarlySundays
Eimer Birkbeck

BIENNIAL VISITOR CENTRE,
52 RENSHAW STREET, L1 4EN
10.30–11.30

Sound artist Eimer will absorb you within urban soundscapes and bring her own perspective to the works within the exhibition.

For booking see page 211.

Cry Me a River

A solo-climate-summit by Anna Mendelssohn

INTERNATIONAL GALLERY,
34 SLATER STREET, L1 4BX
25–27 SEPTEMBER
SEE WWW.THEARTORGANISATION.CO.UK
FOR DETAILS

Cry Me a River

A solo-climate-summit by Anna Mendelssohn

INTERNATIONAL GALLERY,
34 SLATER STREET, L1 4BX
25–27 SEPTEMBER
SEE WWW.THEARTORGANISATION.CO.UK
FOR DETAILS

e-space co-lab International *Art in the Cities* & *X-positions*

THE BLUECOAT, SCHOOL LANE, L1 3BX
11.00
FREE ADMISSION (TICKETS FROM THE BLUECOAT RECEPTION)

e-space co-lab will present live art projects by artists in Liverpool and Shanghai working on the theme of the Expo 2010 'Better City, Better Life' (referencing the UK, Liverpool and China Pavilions). For more information please see www.e-spacelab.net

e-spacelab, curatorial team of Shanghai Biennial on-line conversation with Liverpool Biennial, 6 August, 2010

TOUCHED TALK
Ed Baxter
Whistle in the Dark

BIENNIAL VISITOR CENTRE, 52 RENSHAW STREET, L1 4EN
18.30
FREE ADMISSION. RESERVATION IS RECOMMENDED THROUGH
WWW.BIENNIAL.COM OR 0845 220 2800

Whistle in the Dark is a conversation about community radio and recorded music with Ed Baxter, programming director of the award-winning radio station Resonance FM, moderated by Glenn Boulter. Baxter riffs on Freud's assertion that music arises from paranoia and explores the stage as a method of articulating concerns with both hygiene and currency.

Ed Baxter has written for *The Wire, The Guardian, Variant* and *The Edinburgh Review*, and co-edited *The Complete Works of Thomas De Quincey*. Ed is an associate lecturer in Sound Arts and Design at the London College of Communication. He makes radiophonic art, usually as part of the Resonance Radio Orchestra. His recent works include 'RadioYesterday' (with Dan Scott) and 'Overheard' (with Chris Weaver). He is currently working on a conceptual audio artwork entitled 'Score for Open-Heart Surgery on Charlie Watts'. Ed has produced hundreds of concerts with the likes of Alvin Lucier, Otomo Yoshihide, Faust and Pierre Henry. His favourite new band is Kinnie the Explorer, a group of 18-year-olds from Dorset.

www.resonancefm.com

Co-produced with Glenn Boulter and supported by PRS for Music Foundation's New Music Plus.

Liverpool Artists' Book Fair 2010

A FOUNDATION,
67 GREENLAND STREET,
L1 0BY
12.00–18.00

The third Liverpool Artists' Book Fair will take place during the Liverpool Biennial alongside three exhibitions at A Foundation Liverpool. The fair will be a vibrant platform for stall-holders to present an extraordinary array of artists' books, zines and other paper-based works. Visitors will be able to buy unique and limited editions and also participate in talks, performances and networking opportunities.

For more information about the event contact Clare Warren on
+44 (0)151 706 0600 /
info@afoundation.org.uk

Publish & be Damned, 2006

Early Sundays
Samantha Jones

BIENNIAL VISITOR CENTRE,
52 RENSHAW STREET,
L1 4EN
10.30–11.30

Biennial mediator
Samantha Jones leads
a public realm and
exhibition tour revealing
her personal perspective
on the Biennial theme
Touched.

For booking see page 211.

Art School Alternatives
A *Corridor8* Symposium

LIVERPOOL JOHN MOORES UNIVERSITY, 2 DUCKINFIELD STREET, L3 5RD
10.00–18.00
FOR MORE INFORMATION AND RESERVATIONS VISIT
WWW.CORRIDOR8.CO.UK

Is school a place, an institution, a set of facilities, a
situation, a circumstance, an attitude, or a constellation
of relationships of the transfer of acquired, invented, and
accumulated knowledge…?

Raqs Media Collective, 'Art School: Propositions for the 21st Century', MIT Press (2009)

Drawing together a range of practitioners whose work looks
to the communal, collaborative and participatory, *Corridor8*
contemporary visual art magazine presents a dynamic symposium
that explores methods of learning and ideas of schooling.

SPEAKERS INCLUDE:
Department 21
irational.org
Feral Trade
Islington Mill Art Academy
Circa Projects
Black Dogs
A Latento
No Fixed Abode
Disrupt Dominant Frequencies
Artmarket/Kunstfreund

The symposium also includes a preview of new film work by
Paul Rooney.

City Limits
Sky Arts Artichoke Salon Series

WILLIAMSON TUNNELS HERITAGE CENTRE
18.45–20.00
£7/£4 (CONCESSIONS), BOOKING REQUIRED
TO BOOK CALL +44 (0)151 702 7400 OR VISIT
WWW.TATE.ORG.UK/LIVERPOOL/EVENTSEDUCATION/TALKSDISCUSSIONS/

Are large-scale public events nothing more than a waste of resources and a drain on the public purse? Do they place an unbearable strain on our cities? Or are they a vital part of urban life?

Artichoke, producers of live events such as *La Machine* and Antony Gormley's *One & Other*, are collaborating with Sky Arts and Tate to mount the second in a series of three public conversations about the nature and use of public space. In the wake of Liverpool '08 (European Capital of Culture) and as the sixth Liverpool Biennial explores how art touches a city, curator and writer Tim Marlow chairs a panel of provocative speakers to consider the impact of such events on the life and work of the population.

In the extraordinary surroundings of the Williamson Tunnels, we examine the true legacy of the programme of events that transformed Liverpool, and ask how much a city can really take, particularly in a time of cuts to public services. We consider if there really is any lasting benefit, and if so, how it can be harnessed for the future.

Tours of the Williamson Tunnels will be available on the night.

Aurélien Froment
Pulmo Marina

Short film screening with *A Town Called Panic* (dir. Stéphane Aubier and Vincent Patar)

FACT, 88 WOOD STRRET, L1 4DQ
8–14 OCTOBER

See page 214.

www.fact.co.uk for screening times and prices.

The Innovasion
An alternate reality game

WWW.BIENNIAL.COM/INNOVASION
8.00–22.00

Something is wrong at the Liverpool Biennial. Suspicious signs and mysterious codes appear from nowhere, and a sinister conspiracy is lurking in the shadows. But the good thing is: You can be part of it! Immerse yourself in a new world, find the trail, unravel the mystery, break the codes and help save the world. Your creativity is under threat. This is only the beginning.

Join our pervasive alternate reality game. For more information and to sign up for the game see www.biennial.com/innovasion.

Co-produced with Hope Street Ltd.

Curator's Exhibition Tour
Sara-Jayne Parsons

THE BLUECOAT, SCHOOL LANE, L1 3BX
14.00
FREE (TICKETS FROM THE BLUECOAT RECEPTION)

Sara-Jayne Parsons, Exhibitions Curator at the Bluecoat, leads a tour discussing the work on display for *Touched*.

Liverpool Live Event
Bed-In at the Bluecoat

THE BLUECOAT, SCHOOL LANE, L1 3BX
UNTIL 9 DECEMBER
VARIOUS TIMES
FREE ADMISSION

9 October would have been John Lennon's 70th birthday and 9 December is thirty years since his assassination. The Bluecoat marks these anniversaries by recreating John and Yoko's famous 1969 peace protest. Each day a bed in our Hub will host a new action by performers, artists and others – selected from an open call – for a better world.

Part of Liverpool's John Lennon Tribute Season.

© Trintity Mirror

Early Sundays
Eleanor Reese

BIENNIAL VISITOR CENTRE,
52 RENSHAW STREET,
L1 4EN (STARTING POINT)
10.30–11.30

Eleanor Reese, writer and
poet, will take you on a
take a poetic experience
as she responds to the
theme and exhibition of
Touched.

For booking see page 211.

Shang-Pool Arcadia

WWW.SHANG-POOL.COM

Shang-Pool Arcadia is a collaborative research project between
Shanghai and Liverpool John Moores universities. Using virtual
and mixed realities, it explores the notion of the idyll and green
spaces within the city as places of recreation, contemplation,
nourishment and meeting places. The research will also seek to
align itself with Liverpool Biennial's projects in areas of urban
regeneration in Merseyside and consider similar projects in
Shanghai. Realised in partnership with Liverpool Biennial, FACT
and the University of Salford.

Stanley Arcadia is available to explore as an avatar via our website
www.shang-pool.com from 15 October.

See also pages 232 and 236.

Deimantas Narkevicius
Ausgetraumt

Short film screening with *Animal Kingdom* (dir. David Michôd)

FACT, 88 WOOD STREET, L1 4DQ
15–21 OCTOBER

See page 214

www.fact.co.uk for screening times and prices.

Chapter & Verse Literature Festival
Touched Weekender

THE BLUECOAT, SCHOOL LANE, L1 3BX
VARIOUS TIMES AND PRICES
FOR A FULL PROGRAMME PLEASE CONTACT THE BLUECOAT
ON +44 (0)151 702 5324 WWW.BTHEBLUECOAT.ORG.UK

The Bluecoat's annual Chapter & Verse literature festival features talks, readings, workshops and much more. This year it responds to the Biennial theme with a '*Touched* Weekender', including a range of writers who revivify mind, body and soul. Much of the programme goes beyond conventional ways to experience literature, the power of the word to touch being experienced for instance through music performance, cabaret, songwriting, political commentary and debate.

Sunday **17** October

Brian Catling
Cyclops

FREE, LIMITED CAPACITY
THE BLUECOAT, SCHOOL LANE, L1 3BX
13.00–19.00

Brian Catling will respond to the *Touched* theme by testing the boundary between curiosity and repulsion through the manifestation of his performance persona Cyclops. Invited to overcome the uncertainties of interacting with this one-eyed spectre, audiences may observe the Cyclops roaming the streets of Liverpool pursued by the paparazzi, or peer from the balcony into his zoo-like enclosure at the Bluecoat.

Artist, filmmaker, poet and academic, Catling's work oscillates between monumental symbolism and jet-black humour.

Chapter & Verse Literature Festival
Touched Weekender

THE BLUECOAT, SCHOOL LANE, L1 3BX
VARIOUS TIMES AND PRICES

Early Sundays
Jonathon Hering
and aPAtT

BIENNIAL VISITOR CENTRE,
52 RENSHAW STREET,
L1 4EN (STARTING POINT)
10.30–11.30

Jonathan Hering and aPAtT, Live music composers and performers will be providing a live, specially-composed soundtrack/ interpretation for their *Touched* tour.

Jonathan Hering is participating in New Music Plus... developed by the PRS for Music Foundation in association with the Hub, supported by Paul Hamlyn Foundation, Arts Council England and Sound and Music.

For booking see page 211.

TOUCHED TALK
Franco 'Bifo' Berardi
Acceleration of the Infosphere, psychopathology and the ambiguity of therapy

BIENNIAL VISITOR CENTRE, 52 RENSHAW STREET, L1 4EN
18.30
FREE ADMISSION. RESERVATION IS RECOMMENDED THROUGH
WWW.BIENNIAL.COM OR 0845 220 2800

We can reach every point in the world but, more importantly, we can be reached from any point in the world. Privacy and its possibilities are abolished. Attention is under siege everywhere. Not silence but uninterrupted noise, not the red desert, but a cognitive space overcharged with nervous incentives to act: this is the alienation of our times...

from *The Soul at Work*

To be touched increasingly means to be in touch. Franco Berardi Bifo is a writer, media-theorist and media-activist. Over many years he has analysed the relation between the changing nature of work and the increasing use by capitalism of communication technologies and culture to generate value out of our creativity and emotions. In this lecture he will discuss sensibility and the psychopathology implied in the connective mutation of the general intellect. What are the possibilities for a therapy that is conceived in terms of social control to become a new path of autonomisation from the capitalist domination of the mind?

Franco Berardi founded the magazine *A/traverso* (1975-1981) and was part of the staff of *Radio Alice*, the first free pirate radio station in Italy (1976-1978). Like other intellectuals involved in the political movement of *Autonomia* in Italy during the 1970s, he fled to Paris, where he worked with Felix Guattari in the field of schizoanalysis. From his numerous publications *Felix, Precarious Rhapsody* and *The Soul at Work* have appeared in English.

Andy Holden
Three Short Works in Time

VICTORIA GALLERIES AND
MUSEUM, ASHTON STREET,
UNIVERSITY OF LIVERPOOL,
L69 3DR
TWO PERFOMANCES: 13.30
& 18.30
WWW.LIV.AC.UK/VGM

Three Short Works in Time is Andy Holden's ongoing programme of pieces that investigate the relationship between sculptural objects and duration. There is something about this work that incorporates 16mm film, live camera feed, spoken word, and a string quartet performing music by The Grubby Mitts conducted by Johnny Parry.

Liverpool Live Event
Nightmare Before Valentine

THE BLUECOAT, SCHOOL LANE,
L1 3BX
20.00–21.00
£7/£5

This performance the breathtaking
Früchte Im Koma marks the UK
debut for this astonishing Berlin-
based dance company. Featuring
exquisite choreography, bold
visuals and a soulful soundtrack
boasting Tom Waits and Ane Brun,
this is inexorably moving and
intense dance created for three
women, three stuffed animals and
a wall.

Drawing with Sound, the Big Draw at Tate Liverpool

TATE LIVERPOOL, ALBERT DOCK,
L3 4BB
13.30–16.30, IN THE STUDIO
ALL ACTIVITIES ARE FREE
ALSO 31 OCTOBER

Ever wondered what music would
look like if it were a drawing?
Families are invited to drop in to
Tate Liverpool's exciting Big Draw
activities during half-term and
experiment in drawing with sound,
inspired by the Liverpool Biennial
exhibition.

Shang-Pool Arcadia
Picnic in Arcadia

THE BLUECOAT, SCHOOL LANE,
L1 3BX
12.00–17.00

Featuring a live link to Folk
Museum Shanghai.

Nightmare Before Valentine

Early Sundays
Frances Loeffler

BIENNIAL VISITOR CENTRE,
52 RENSHAW STREET,
L1 4EN
(STARTING POINT)
10.30–11.30

Frances Loeffler, assistant curator at Liverpool Biennial, leads a public realm and exhibition tour revealing her personal perspective on the Biennial theme *Touched*, the works of Kris Martin, Laura Belem and other biennial projects.

For booking see page 211.

TOUCHED TALK
AbdouMaliq Simone

BIENNIAL VISITOR CENTRE, 52 RENSHAW STREET, L1 4EN
18.30
FREE ADMISSION. RESERVATION IS RECOMMENDED THROUGH
WWW.BIENNIAL.COM OR 0845 220 2800

AbdouMaliq Simone is an urbanist and Professor of Sociology at Goldsmiths College, London. In his latest book, *City Life from Djakarta to Dakar: Movements at the crossroads* (2010), he describes the surprising ecologies of everyday life in some of the fastest-growing urban centres in the world. What happens when bodies, materials and affect intersect in these global cities of the South broadens our understanding of what cities are and could be. This is not to say the direction of change has shifted, rather that urban development today is part of the global circulation of ideas and stories of what is possible to do in cities. In and among ducking and diving is imagination and resilience and an acute sense that difference and diversity are critical if, in future, people in cities are to thrive.

Marcus Coates
Journey to the Lower World

THE WALKER, WILLIAM BROWN STREET, L3 8EL
13.00–14.00
SUITABLE FOR STUDENTS & ADULTS.
COLLECT A FREE TICKET FROM THE WALKER WELCOME DESK
OR CALL +44 (0)151 478 4697.
WWW.LIVERPOOLMUSEUMS.ORG.UK

Marcus Coates's artwork *Journey to the Lower World*, screening at the Walker from 1 August 2010–early 2011, is a recent major purchase under the Contemporary Art Society's Acquisitions Scheme. Marcus discusses this work, which was made with residents of Liverpool's Sheil Park estate, and more recent projects.

A Contemporary Art Society Centenary Event.

1910—2010
CENTENARY PROGRAMME
**contemporary
art society**

Walker
Art Gallery

LOTTERY FUNDED

Thursday 28 October

David Sherry Performance & Private View of DEADPAN

THE ROYAL STANDARD
18.00.
VISIT WWW.THE-ROYAL-STANDARD.COM FOR PERFORMANCE TIMES.

Mimicking the machismo and seriousness of 1970s live art, David Sherry's surprising and darkly humorous performances look at momentary interactions, pushing real life away from comfort towards observation.

e-space co-lab International *Art in the Cities* & *X-positions*

THE BLUECOAT, SCHOOL LANE, L1 3BX
11.00
FREE ADMISSION (TICKETS FROM THE BLUECOAT RECEPTION)

A live link across the Liverpool Biennial and Shanghai Biennale programmes drawing together some of the open themes generated so far. For more information see www.e-spacelab.net

Friday 29 October

Amar Kanwar *A Love Story*

Short film screening with *The Arbour* (dir. Clio Barnard)

FACT, 88 WOOD STREET, L1 4DQ
29 OCTOBER–4 NOVEMBER

See page 214.

www.fact.co.uk for screening times and prices.

The Marx Lounge in Conversation
Alfredo Jaar – David Harvey and What, How & for Whom/WHW

BIENNIAL VISITOR CENTRE, 52 RENSHAW STREET, L1 4EN
14.00
FREE ADMISSION. RESERVATION IS RECOMMENDED THROUGH
WWW.BIENNIAL.COM OR 0845 220 2800

As part of *The Marx Lounge* Alfredo Jaar engages speakers from the world of political theory and art to think about the ongoing significance of Marx in their work and in the world.

David Harvey is Distinguished Professor of Anthropology at the City University of New York Graduate School and former Professor of Geography at Johns Hopkins and Oxford Universities. The author of numerous books, he was awarded the Patron's Medal of the Royal Geographical Society in 1995 and elected to the American Academy of Arts and Sciences in 2007. His latest books are *The Enigma of Capital* and *A Companion to Marx's Capital*. A revised edition of his seminal *Social Justice and the City* was published in 2009. He is the world's most cited academic geographer and his course on Marx's *Capital* has been downloaded by well over 750,000 people since mid-2008: http://davidharvey.org/

What, How & for Whom/WHW is a curatorial collective formed in 1999 and based in Zagreb, Croatia. Its members are Ivet Ćurlin, Ana Dević, Nataša Ilić and Sabina Sabolović, and designer and publicist Dejan Kršić. WHW organizes a range of production, exhibition and publishing projects and since 2003 has been directing city-owned Gallery Nova in Zagreb. *What, how* and *for whom*, the three basic questions of every economic organization, concern the planning, concept and realization of exhibitions as well as the production and distribution of artworks and the artist's position in the labor market. These questions formed the title of WHW's first project dedicated to the 152nd anniversary of the *Communist Manifesto*, in 2000 in Zagreb, and became the motto of WHW's work and the title of the collective. In 2009 WHW was curator of the 11th Istanbul Biennial 'What Keeps Mankind Alive?'

Early Sundays
Jonathan Raisin

BIENNIAL VISITOR CENTRE,
52 RENSHAW STREET, L1 4EN
(STARTING POINT)

10.30–11.30

Composer Jonathan has created a musical composition in response to *Touched* – join Jonathan to experience a unique *Touched* tour.

For booking see page 211.

TOUCHED TALK
Nina Power
The Wound of Work
BIENNIAL VISITOR CENTRE, 52 RENSHAW STREET, L1 4EN
18.30
FREE ADMISSION. RESERVATION IS RECOMMENDED THROUGH
WWW.BIENNIAL.COM OR 0845 220 2800

This talk will address how contemporary work relates to both art
and feminism, with a particular focus on contemporary modes of
employment and consumerism. The body, as discussed by Hervé
Juvin in his recent book *The Coming of the Body*, will be the
starting point for an exploration of what it means when the body
comes to stand in for the end of history, and how work and the
body relate to one another in the present.

Nina Power is a senior lecturer in philosophy at Roehampton
University and the author of *One-Dimensional Woman*
(Zero Books, 2009).

Liverpool Live Event
Richard Haynes:
Listen My Secret Fetish
THE BLUECOAT, SCHOOL LANE, L1 3BX
20.00–21.00
£7/£5

A hybrid live art club act-cum-queer concert recital. Musical
wunderkind and exhibitionist Richard Haynes explores
contemporary music and sexual fetish through a collection
of strangely tantalising sound pieces. Extreme new sounds,
compromising circumstances and physically demanding scenarios
characterise these 'four fetishes' for solo clarinet.

Contains nudity and adult themes.

Presented by Homotopia

Keren Cytter
The Coat
Short film screening with
Another Year
(dir. Mike Leigh)

FACT, 88 WOOD STREET,
L1 4DX
5–11 NOVEMBER

See page 214.

www.fact.co.uk for
screening times and prices.

Shang-Pool Arcadia
Picnic in Arcadia
THE BLUECOAT,
SCHOOL LANE, L1 3BX
12.00–17.00

Featuring a live link to Folk
Museum Shanghai.

See page 229.

Richard Haynes: *Listen My Secret Fetish*

Liverpool Live Event
Rhys Chatham
Die Donnergötter and *Guitar Trio*

THE BLUECOAT, SCHOOL LANE, L1 3BX
20.00–22.00
£10

Best known for large-scale works like *A Crimson Grail for 400 Guitars*, Chatham trained with La Monte Young before becoming a leading exponent of New York's No Wave scene. Here he performs his acclaimed *Guitar Trio* with Liverpool University music students and his rarely heard 1985 work *Die Donnergötter*. The ensemble is mirrored in a new composition by Jonathan Hering (aPAtT), opening the concert with a piece for synthesiser, guitar, bass and drum sounds.

The concert is preceded by free day-time events: an interactive soundscape by the HIVE Collective based on the 100 greatest guitar riffs of all time, and mallet-guitar performances by Ex-Easter Island Heads at 15.00, 17.00 & 19.00.

Supported by PRS for Music Foundation's New Music Plus and Liverpool University.

Part of Liverpool Music Week

Presented by Samizdat

Rhys Chatham

Early Sundays
Amanprit Sandhu

BIENNIAL VISITOR CENTRE,
52 RENSHAW STREET,
L1 4EN (STARTING POINT)
10.30–11.30

Amanprit Sandhu, curatorial assistant at Liverpool Biennial, leads a public realm and exhibition tour revealing her personal perspective on the Biennial theme *Touched*.

For booking see page 211.

Curator's Exhibition Tour
Lorenzo Fusi

BIENNIAL VISITOR CENTRE,
52 RENSHAW STREET,
L1 4EN (STARTING POINT)
18.30

Lorenzo Fusi, curator Liverpool Biennial, will lead a talk/discussion and walk-around of *The Human Stain*.

Liverpool Live Event
Minton/Nicols/Boyland

THE BLUECOAT,
SCHOOL LANE, L1 3BX
20.00–21.30
£9/£7

Diving headlong into
uncharted territory,
three of the UK's most
electrifying improvising
vocalists enter a world of
soaring wails, hysterical
jabbers and sublime drones.
Inspired by an incendiary
debut at Hearing Voices
2007 and rooted in a
creative association
spanning three decades,
the performers explore the
emotive potential of the
human voice.

Super Gimp
A new play written by C. Pike
Directed by C. Pike & Anna Levin

PHASE 5, 39 SEEL ST, L1
ALSO 12, 13 NOVEMBER
SEE WWW.THEARTORGANISATION.CO.UK FOR DETAILS

Super Gimp presents us with three characters locked in a deathly
embrace. Leonard has a five-minute memory span but has the
potential to evolve depending on questions put to him between
each relapse. Super Gimp has convinced himself that if he can
make Leonard understand his existence he can move on, but
twenty-two years of trying have yielded no progress. The trio is
completed by the Stranger, an entity who plagues Leonard during
each relapse and thwarts Super Gimp's efforts. Super Gimp is
a play that deals with issues of mortality and eternity with dark
humour and great truth.

Liverpool Film Night

FACT, 88 WOOD STREET, L1 4DQ
18.30

Selected in response to *Touched*. We'll be showcasing the latest
and greatest in local film making selected from open submission.

Dadafest
Animal
Sunaura Taylor

ST GEORGE'S HALL,
ST GEORGE'S PLACE, L1 1JJ
12 NOVEMBER–
3 DECEMBER
FREE

Paintings centred on the
relationship between
freaks-show images,
medical photographs and
butchers' diagrams.

Blackbird, Pics & Artificial Grass

THE BLUECOAT, SCHOOL
LANE, L1 3BX
ALSO 13 NOVEMBER
19.30

Performance artists
Marina Tsarstara, Tamar
Daly and Sara Popowa,
who have been completing
a residency together in
Liverpool, bring together
their individual concerns
in the fields of visual art,
movement and dance for
this performance.

Expect a colourful and
unusual blend of live,
installed and participatory
pieces, themed around the
extensions of our physical
and social bodies.

Dadafest
Alexa Wright
Cover Story

ST GEORGE'S HALL, ST GEORGE'S PLACE, L1 1JJ
12 NOVEMBER–3 DECEMBER
FREE

Wright's work explores the way that a person's identity is
constructed in the mind of the observer, drawing attention to the
significance that is still attributed to both 'normal' and 'abnormal'
human faces and to the impulse to classify people in terms of
gender, race, age, ability and social status. The video installation is
made up of visual images and language, but the visual information
can't be made to correspond to the image of the 'other' generated
by the text. *Cover Story* was made with the help of five women
who have severe facial deformities – genetic or acquired. The
narrative in the work is a compilation of excerpts from interviews
with these women.

Liverpool Live Event
Keith Hennessy
Crotch

THE BLUECOAT, SCHOOL LANE, L1 3BX
20.00–21.00
£9/£7

A searing and uncompromising solo by San Francisco-based Keith
Hennessy – international performer, choreographer, sex-positive
mentor, and master of ceremonies. His award-winning work
draws on live art, circus, improvisation, activism and shamanism.
'Hennessy's presence burns; he ignites any subject he tackles...'
San Francisco Weekly.

The Marx Lounge in Conversation
Alfredo Jaar – Chantal Mouffe

BIENNIAL VISITOR CENTRE, 52 RENSHAW STREET, L1 4EN
18.30
FREE ADMISSION. RESERVATION IS RECOMMENDED THROUGH
WWW.BIENNIAL.COM OR 0845 220 2800

As part of *The Marx Lounge* Alfredo Jaar engages speakers from the
world of political theory and art to think about the ongoing significance
of Marx in their work and in the world.

Chantal Mouffe is Professor of Political Theory at the University of
Westminster. She authored numerous books among which are (with
Ernesto Laclau) *Hegemony and Socialist Strategy: Towards a
Radical Democratic Politics* (1985); *The Return of the Political*
(1993), *The Democratic Paradox* (2000) and *On the Political* (2005).
She is currently elaborating a non-rationalist approach to political theory;
formulating an 'agonistic' model of democracy; and engaged in research
projects on the rise of right-wing populism in Europe and the place of
Europe in a multipolar world order

Early Sundays
Chris Ball

BIENNIAL VISITOR CENTRE,
52 RENSHAW STREET, L1 4EN
(STARTING POINT)
10.30–11.30

Drama and education
specialist Chris Ball
will engage you in an
experiential tour of the
Touched exhibition.

For booking see page 211.

TOUCHED TALK
Simon Critchley
Fireflies

BIENNIAL VISITOR CENTRE, 52 RENSHAW STREET,
L1 4EN
18.30
FREE ADMISSION. RESERVATION IS RECOMMENDED THROUGH
WWW.BIENNIAL.COM OR 0845 220 2800

Is anger the first political emotion? *In Infinitely Demanding*
(2007) the philosopher Simon Critchley identifies a massive
political disappointment at the heart of liberal democracy and
argues for an ethics of commitment that can inform a radical
politics. In this talk Critchley discusses the infinite demands
of art and his growing interests in collaborative practices in
relation to art and politics.

Simon Critchley is chair of the Department of Philosophy at the
New School for Social Research. His recent books include *The
Book of Dead Philosophers* (2009) and *On Heidegger's
Being and Time* (2008).

Liverpool Live Event
**Triple Bill including
Club Fisk and
Augusto Corrieri**

THE BLUECOAT, SCHOOL
LANE, L1 3BX
22.00–21.30
£7/£5

A brilliant and entertaining
evening of cutting-edge
dance. Club Fisk's
Forestillinger consists of
two dancers undertaking
a hilariously elaborate
lecture-demonstration of a
postmodern performance.
In Augusto Corrieri's
Quartet the movements,
objects, music and words
of a solo are performed
in isolation, one after the
other.

Presented by MDI

Club Fisk

LONG NIGHT
**18TH NOVEMBER 2010
WWW.CULTURE.ORG.UK**

This year the popular Long Night returns on Thursday 18
November. Visitors will be able to enjoy events from 4pm
until late. Over 50 venues in Liverpool city centre are offering
you a great evening of visual arts and culture. Liverpool
Biennial 2010 venues will be open late, so please check
www.biennial.com and for further information about the
Long Night visit www.culture.org.uk or pick up a brochure
nearer the time.

Long Night
Sound Relay

PHILHARMONIC HALL, TATE LIVERPOOL
AND LOCATIONS THROUGHOUT THE CITY
19.00–22.00
FREE ADMISSION

Join the magnetic relay of sound as musicians including
Ensemble 10/10 and the aPAtT Orchestra take you on a
cumulative journey of musical happenings from Hope Street
to the Albert Dock.

Inspired by the Tate Liverpool *Touched* exhibition as part
of the Liverpool Biennial, and taking composer Jennifer
Watson's *Reflections* as its focus, musicians test the
limits of their own practice to create a series of surprising,
experimental and reflexive happenings. Follow the Long
Night trail as the procession gathers pace, picking up new
musical material along the way.

Starting at the Royal Liverpool Philharmonic foyer at 19.00,
the relay gathers momentum with performances at Rapid,
FACT and the Bluecoat before making its final journey to Tate
Liverpool with music in the galleries, including in and around
the installation of Magdalena Abakanowicz's *Embryology*
(1978–80).

Art in Mind: Philosophy in Pubs

TATE, ALBERT DOCK, L3 4BB
GROUP RECEPTION ROOM
19.00–21.00
FREE, NO BOOKING REQUIRED

Art touches a city, but how does it touch you? Philosophy in Pubs bring their philosophy café to Tate Liverpool for Art in Mind, a series of special enquiries around Tate's temporary Exhibitions. This session focuses on the sixth Liverpool Biennial: *Touched*. Everyone has philosophical thoughts and as a group we would like to hear yours – whoever you are, wherever you're from and whatever they may be! Join this informal group for those with an interest in talking about the wonder of art (or listening to other people talk about it). No academic or philosophical background is necessary. Just turn up and enjoy.

www.philosophyinpubs.org.uk

Sonia Khurana
Lying-down-on-the-ground

THE WALKER, L1
18.00–22.00
WWW.LIVERPOOLMUSEUMS.ORG.UK/WALKER/
SEE PAGE 219.

DaDaFest
DaDaFest International 2010
Opening
18 NOVEMBER–3 DECEMBER
WWW.DADAFEST2010.CO.UK

Opening of the tenth edition of DaDaFest, the UK's first and largest Disability and Deaf Arts festival, brings artists from across the globe to Liverpool to showcase and celebrate the best in Disability and Deaf Arts. DaDaFest International 2010 presents art from a unique cultural perspective by challenging and entertaining audiences with the theme *Objects of Curiosity and Desire*, curated by Artistic Director Garry Robson.

Among the exhibitions, performances, films, workshops and talks you'll find work by a surreal Beatles Tribute Band that screams at the audience, startling images from Mumbai's blind photographers, a Ugandan Krip Hop star, Goth puppets from Australia, a Singing/Signing Choir and the UK premier of GIMP, an inclusive dance work that has taken America by storm.

The Festival programme will be announced in September.

DaDaFest is produced by DaDa – Disability & Deaf Arts.

Simon Mckeown

Objects of Curiosity and Desire
THE BLUECOAT, SCHOOL LANE, L1 3BX

Exhibition exploring the human body, its quirks, questions and endless fascinations, *Objects of Curiosity and Desire* presents work in a range of media with:

Tom Shakespeare

Yinka Shonibare
Yinka Shonibare's work lampoons and undermines notions of cultural authenticity. Simultaneously innocent and subversive he addresses a range of cultural and historical issues, blurring the boundaries of design, ethnography, and contemporary art.

Simon Mckeown
Simon Mckeown's new video in his Motion Disabled series integrates motion capture and 3D animation, highlighting the intricacies and uniqueness of individuals' physicality.

Tom Shakespeare
Tom Shakespeare's highly stylised photographs, based on historical paintings, examine birth, death and the vulnerability of embodiment.

Touched: Philosophy Meets Art

A one-day conference organised by the Philosophy Department, University of Liverpool and Liverpool Biennial

VICTORIA GALLERIES AND MUSEUM
ASHTON STREET, UNIVERSITY OF LIVERPOOL, L69 3DR
9.30–17.00

FEES: (including coffee/lunch): Early Registration (until 19/10/10) £10; Late Registration: £20. Student bursaries available.

REGISTRATION FORM: please visit, www.liv.ac.uk/philosophy/index.htm

ENQUIRIES AND BURSARY APPLICATIONS: please contact Dr Panayiota Vassilopoulou, Tel: 0151 7942787; email: yiota@liv.ac.uk

Some of the most prevalent views in the history of philosophy and art have suggested that philosophy and art are both devoted to the discovery of 'universal' truths and should result in works, textual or non-textual, that must remain 'untouched': their value must defy time and transcend space. Yet neither philosophy nor art can be divorced from concrete experience and they both make a claim on our thinking and being – on our most refined concepts and reasoning as well as our most unrefined desires, emotions and dreams. The distance between 'knowing oneself' and 'making oneself' seems blurred, and to get our bearings we turn to philosophy and to art: they both issue in forms of experience that intensely influence the way we situate ourselves in the world, the way we construct our personal, community, and cultural identities.

We ask: is there a role for *touching* in the aesthetic division of labour, which is indisputably dominated by the seeing and hearing that seem to safeguard the distance between the work of art and us? How would this change the set of metaphors that still guide our understanding of artistic creation and reception? And then a question of unexpected resonance: are we touched by Art? How do works of art transform the way we understand and form our identities? And indeed, do art festivals such as the Biennial prompt personal, cultural, and social change?

SPEAKERS:
Prof. Berys Gaut (St Andrews); Prof. Sue Golding (Greenwich); Prof. Matthew Kieran (Leeds); Prof. Derek Matravers (Open University); Prof. Peter Osborne (Kingston); Dr Panayiota Vassilopoulou (Liverpool).

Supported by The British Society of Aesthetics, The Mind Association, The Royal Institute of Philosophy, The Department of Philosophy and the School of Arts, University of Liverpool.

Liverpool Live Event
Mandy Romero
Stevenage

THE BLUECOAT, SCHOOL LANE, L1 3BX
20.00–21.30
£6/£4

Epiphanies come in unexpected
forms. In 1968 a young man's
life was changed forever by the
cinematic-romp *Here We Go
Round the Mulberry Bush*,
when he ran away to Stevenage.
Using film, live performance and
installation, Liverpool-based
transgender artist Mandy Romero
retraces these steps through the
'new' landscapes of forty years ago.

Presented by Homotopia

Sunday **21** November

Early Sundays
John Hughes

BIENNIAL VISITOR CENTRE,
52 RENSHAW STREET, L1 4EN
(STARTING POINT) 10.30–11.30

Poet and storyteller John Hughes
will take you on a narrative journey
to engage you in the theme and
exhibition of *Touched*.

For booking see page 211.

e-space co-lab
International
Art in the Cities &
X-positions

THE BLUECOAT, SCHOOL LANE, L1 3BX
11.00
FREE ADMISSION (TICKETS FROM THE
BLUECOAT RECEPTION)

A 'Biennials dialogue' relating to the
public domain, structured through
art explorations by Shanghai- and
Liverpool-based artists relating
to *Touched* (Liverpool) and
Rehearsal (Shanghai).
For more information please see
www.e-spacelab.net/

Mandy Romero: *Stevenage*

The Artists Cinema introduced by Mike Sperlinger

FACT, **88** WOOD STREET, L1 **4**DX
18.30
£4/£3 (MEMBERS AND CONCESSIONS)

This screening collects all six of the Artists Cinema films showing during the Biennial, together with a film made for the Artists Cinema series by Catherine Sullivan with Farhad Sharmini. Having been shown before general release films at FACT, here the films are shown together in a single screening, introduced by Benjamin Cook, Director at LUX, the UK's pre-eminent agency for artists' moving image. A Q&A session following the films with Cook, FACT curator Heather Corcoran and the audience will focus on the context of moving image in the gallery and the cinema, and a phenomenological approach to moving image in relation to the *Touched* theme of the Biennial.

DaDaFest in association with FACT
Roy Stringer Lecture Stelarc

FACT, **88** WOOD STREET, L1 **4**DX
FOR TIMES AND PRICES SEE
WWW.FACT.CO.UK

Probably best known for having an ear transplated onto his arm, this influential Australian-based performance artist incorporates themes of cyborgisation and other human–machine interfaces in his work. Stelarc will be in conversation with Liz Carr in the third of a programme of annual lectures in honour of FACT's late Chairman Roy Stringer.

DaDaFest
The Freak and the Showgirl

THE BLUECOAT, SCHOOL LANE, L1 **3**BX
20.00
£8/£6

In this comic cabaret of striptease, freak show and song, Julie Atlas Muz, Miss Coney Island 2006 and performance artist, and Mat Fraser, film, television and stage actor and presenter, perform their greatest hits, new work, daring duets and hilarious audience participation.

Touched DaDaFest
'The Dark Behind my Eyelids'

THE BLUECOAT, SCHOOL LANE, L1 3BX
9.30–17.30
FREE ADMISSION. BOOKING REQUIRED. FOR MORE INFORMATION
SEE WWW.BIENNIAL.COM OR WWW.DADAFEST2010.CO.UK
OR CALL 0845 220 2800

A conference in collaboration between Liverpool Biennial and
DaDaFest International 10. The title is a quote from Amanda Baggs,
autism human rights activist and prolific blogger (ballastexistenz.
autistics.org). She explained how processing sensory input,
including emotional responses from inside her body, are the main
part of her thinking. Thinking is 'The dark behind my eyelids.
The sensation of pressure on my arms. The sound of rustling'.
Her interlocutor was incredulous, this was 'feeling'.

The conference aims to rethink the relation between art, thinking
and normalcy. What are our assumptions when we distinguish
between thought and feeling, body and brain, identity and
difference? How is (dis)ability marked by these assumptions and
who's interests are served by them in the space of art?

9.30–12.30
Film screenings

The Woman who Thinks Like A Cow (Dr Temple Grandin, USA
2006); Amanda Baggs shorts; *The Sunshine Boy* (Fridrik Thor
Fridriksson, Iceland, 2010).

13–14.30
Conditions of Development

How do the autistic and deaf experiences condition our
conceptions of place, space, object and event. Artist Wendy
Jacob (The Autism Studio, MIT) and architect Hansel Bauman
who directed the DeafSpace project at Gallaudet University,in
conversation with with deaf artist Aaron Williamson.

14.30–15.30
Niet Normaal – Difference on Display

In Spring 2010 the groundbreaking exhibition *Niet Normaal
– Difference on Display* in Amsterdam questioned disability
through an investigation of the concept of normality in
contemporary society. What is normal and who decides?
The initiator and curator Ine Gevers in conversation with artist
Mat Fraser.

16–17.30
**The Beast and the
Sovereign or Questions of
Responsibility**

Who can comment on
issues of difference with
authority? What are
the possibilities for an
articulation of difference
beyond the niche?

With Ute Meta Bauer,
curator and director of the
Visual Art Programme at
MIT, Bryan Biggs, artistic
director the Bluecoat,
Tobin Siebers (tbc), author
of *Disability Aesthetics*,
and others.

Liverpool Live Event
Guillermo Goméz-Peña and Roberto Sifuentes (La Pocha Nostra):
Corpo Ilicito

THE BLUECOAT, SCHOOL LANE, L1 3BX
20.00–22.00
£8/£6

La Pocha Nostra's immersive performances have inspired a devoted international following and were last experienced at the Bluecoat in a legendary performance to open the 2002 Liverpool Biennial. Using their bodies as sites for political reinvention and poetic prophesying, they explore the Bush administration's criminalisation of the brown body and the emerging culture of hope that has developed in response.

A DaDaFest event with Homotopia and MDI

Guillermo Gomez-Pena and Roberto Sifuentes.
Photograph Zach Gross, 200

Early Sundays
Elfin Spurs

BIENNIAL VISITOR CENTRE,
52 RENSHAW STREET,
L1 4EN
(STARTING POINT)
10.30–11.30

Elfin Spurs will take you on the ultimate *Touched* tour. Experience live music, costumes and a wonderful Sunday morning mixture of wit and beauty.

For booking see page 211.

DaDaFest
The Feral Four

THE BLUECOAT,
88 WOOD STREET, L1 4DQ
SEE WWW.DADAFEST2010.
CO.UK FOR MORE
INFORMATION FREE

Hysterical screaming was integral to the Beatles' music and The Feral Four were formed to concentrate upon exploring this theory by screaming at the audience while dressed as a Beatles tribute band.

How to get to/from and around Liverpool

Merseytravel

www.merseytravel.gov.uk
Info Centre: +44 (0)151 227 5181
Ferries: +44 (0)151 330 1444 (bookings)
+44 (0)151 630 1030 (enquiries)
Traveline (for timetable info): 0871 200 2233

Whether you would like to travel by bus, train or ferry, Liverpool and the surrounding area are well served by public transport. The best thing to do when planning your journey is to go to the Merseytravel Journey Planner (click through from the Merseytravel website above). Also available as a smart phone application.

Taxis

Taxis in Liverpool are very reasonably priced. It will only cost a few pounds to get from one venue to another in bad weather. It will cost about £15 to get from Liverpool city centre to Antony Gormley's *Another Place* installation on Crosby Beach (see page 209).

Mersey Cabs (hackney cabs): 0151 298 2222

Other ways to get about and see the exhibition

City Rickshaws operate in Liverpool and can hold up to two people. For more information: 0845 094 2022

Liverpool hop on–hop off bus tours depart from various places, such as Pier Head and The Beatles Story at the Albert Dock. Alternatively call City Sightseeing on 07845 056228 or the City Explorer on +44 (0)151 933 2324/922 4284

The Yellow Duckmarine Company operates a service that takes you around the city centre and into the water at the Salthouse Dock to see Liverpool from a different angle. Call +44 (0)151 708 7799 to book.

1 **Lime Street Big Screen**
Tala Madani
(Irregular screenings)

2 **The Futurist Cinema**
Emese Benczùr

3 **Philips Big Screen**
Tala Madani

4 **52 Renshaw Street**
Julieta Aranda and Anton Vidokle,
Kamelo Bermejo, Rosa Barba,
Tania Bruguera, Minerva Cuevas,
Song Dong, Tim Eitel, Oren Eliav,
Freee, Meschac Gaba, NS Harsha,
Edi Hila, Alfredo Jaar, Allan Kaprow,
Y.Z. Kami, Csaba Kis Róka, Daniel
Knorr, Lee Mingwei, Aimé Mpane,
Ryan Trecartin, Markus Schinwald,
Zbyněk Sedlecký

5 **Visitor Centre** *i*

6 **107 Wood Street Garage**
Raymond Pettibon

7 **FACT**
Tehching Hsieh, Kaarina Kaikkonen,
Meiro Koizumi Minouk Lim,
Yves Netzhammer

8 **Open Eye Gallery**
Lars Laumann

9 **Gable end 24 Fleet Street**
Tala Madani

10 **the Bluecoat**
Daniel Bozhkov, Nicholas Hlobo,
Carol Rama, Ranjani Shettar

11 **Between 84-86 Duke Street**
Do Ho Suh

12 **Mann Island**
Héctor Zamora

A John Moores Painting Prize 2010
Walker Art Gallery

D The Cooperative
28–32 Renshaw Street

● S.Q.U.A.T. Liverpool

Ceri Hand Gallery
12 Cotton Street L3 7DY
(15 mins walk)

The Royal
Vauxhall Be
(5 mins wa

Key

P Parking
P Disabled parking
WC Toilets
NHS NHS walk in centre
Bus station
Train station
Hotel Novotel Liverpool

Turning the
Place Over
Richard Wilson

Town
hall

Liver
Building

Cunard
Building

Port of
Liverpool
Building

Liverpool
One

Chavasse Park

Canning
Dock

5 minute walk

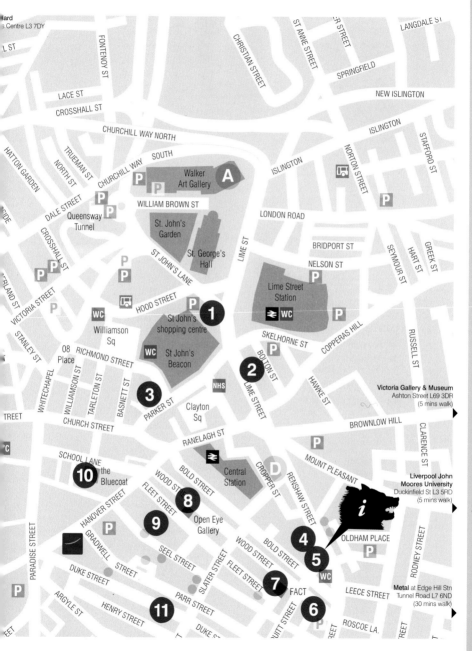

LANGDALE ST

SPRINGFIELD

NEW ISLINGTON

ISLINGTON

STAFFORD ST

Hard
s Centre L3 7DY

L ST

FONTENOY ST

ST ANNE STREET

ER STREET

CHRISTIAN STREET

LACE ST

CROSSHALL ST

HATTON GARDEN

TRUEMAN ST

NORTH ST

CHURCHILL WAY NORTH

CHURCHILL WAY SOUTH

P **P**

Walker
Art Gallery **A**

ISLINGTON

LONDON ROAD

NORTON STREET

P

DALE STREET

P **P**

Queensway
Tunnel

WILLIAM BROWN ST

St. John's
Garden

St. George's
Hall

BRIDPORT ST

NELSON ST

P

SEYMOUR ST

HART ST

GREEK ST

CROSSHALL ST

RLAND ST

VICTORIA STREET

P **P**

P **P**

P

ST JOHN'S LANE

LIME ST

HOOD STREET

P **1**

WC

St John's
shopping centre

Lime Street
Station

≷ WC

P

RUSSELL ST

STANLEY ST

Williamson
Sq

SKELHORNE ST

COPPERAS HILL

08 RICHMOND STREET
Place

WC

St John's
Beacon

BOLTON ST

P

2

HAWKE ST

WHITECHAPEL

WILLIAMSON ST

TARLETON ST

BASNETT ST

3

PARKER ST

NHS

Clayton
Sq

LIME STREET

Victoria Gallery & Museum
Ashton Street L69 3DR
(5 mins walk)

TREET

CHURCH STREET

RANELAGH ST

BROWNLOW HILL

CLARENCE ST

C

SCHOOL LANE

10 the
Bluecoat

WOOD ST

BOLD STREET

≷

Central
Station

CROPPER ST

RENSHAW STREET

P

MOUNT PLEASANT

**Liverpool John
Moores University**
Duckinfield St L3 5RD
(5 mins walk)

PARADISE STREET

HANOVER STREET

FLEET STREET

8

9

Open Eye
Gallery

WOOD STREET

BOLD STREET

4

5

i

OLDHAM PLACE

P

RODNEY STREET

P

GRADWELL STREET

SEEL STREET

SLATER STREET

FLEET STREET

7

6

WC

Metal at Edge Hill Stn
Tunnel Road L7 6ND
(30 mins walk)

DUKE STREET

ARGYLE ST

HENRY STREET

PARR STREET

11

UITT STREET

FACT

LEECE STREET

DUKE S

ROSCOE LA.

REET

EET

253

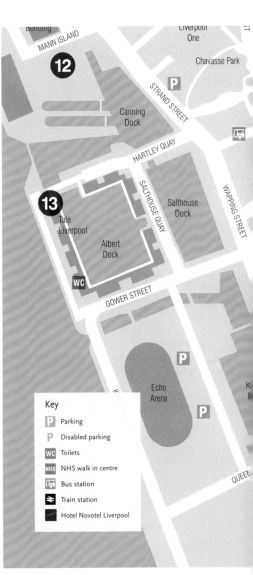

Key

P	Parking
P	Disabled parking
WC	Toilets
NHS	NHS walk in centre
	Bus station
	Train station
	Hotel Novotel Liverpool

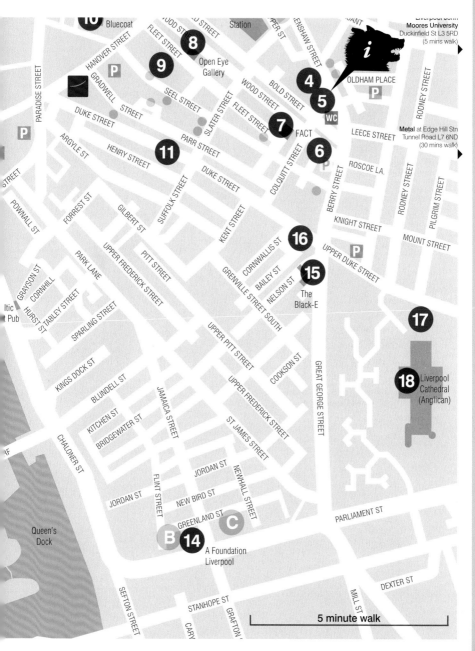

Bluecoat

Fleet Street

Station

Open Eye Gallery

Moores University
Duckinfield St L3 5RD
(5 mins walk)

OLDHAM PLACE

WC

Metal at Edge Hill Stn
Tunnel Road L7 6ND
(30 mins walk)

FACT

LEECE STREET

ROSCOE LA.

BERRY STREET

KNIGHT STREET

MOUNT STREET

The
Black-E

UPPER DUKE STREET

Liverpool
Cathedral
(Anglican)

PARLIAMENT ST

A Foundation
Liverpool

Queen's
Dock

DEXTER ST

5 minute walk

PARADISE STREET
HANOVER STREET
GRADWELL STREET
DUKE STREET
SEEL STREET
SLATER STREET
WOOD STREET
FLEET STREET
BOLD STREET
COLQUITT STREET
RODNEY STREET
PILGRIM STREET
ARGYLE ST
HENRY STREET
PARR STREET
DUKE STREET
KENT STREET
SUFFOLK STREET
FORREST ST
GILBERT ST
PITT STREET
UPPER FREDERICK STREET
GRENVILLE STREET SOUTH
CORNWALLIS ST
BAILEY ST
NELSON ST
PARK LANE
GRAYSON ST
CORNHILL
STABLEY STREET
HURST ST
POWNALL ST
SPARLING STREET
KINGS DOCK ST
BLUNDELL ST
KITCHEN ST
BRIDGEWATER ST
JAMAICA STREET
CHALONER ST
UPPER PITT STREET
COOKSON ST
UPPER FREDERICK STREET
GREAT GEORGE STREET
ST JAMES STREET
JORDAN ST
FLINT STREET
NEW BIRD ST
NEWHALL STREET
GREENLAND ST
JORDAN ST
SEFTON STREET
STANHOPE ST
GRAFTON
MILL ST

Itic
Pub

Touched acknowledgements

Rosa Barba would like to thank Mersey Tunnels, Liverpool, Jerry Reed, Christian Meier, Klimatechnik Lutz, Francesca Venier, Jan St. Werner, Gio Marconi, Carlier I Gebauer and Fraser Arnott. Thanks also to Grosvenor and Edmund Kirby.

Laura Belém would like to thank Fernando Rocha, Eduardo Borges, Matthew Wood and Galeria Luisa Strina. Thanks also to NML.

Emese Benczùr
Thanks to The Futurist and Edward Symmons.

Hector Zamora would like to thank Bonifacio López and his team, Labor Gallery. Lorenzo Fusi, Frances Loeffler, Leon Seth, Rajwant Sandhu, Amanprit Sandhu. Thanks also to Neptune Developments.

Tania Bruguera
Thanks to Grosvenor and Edmund Kirby.

Alfredo Jaar would like to thank Verso Books and News from Nowhere: Liverpool's Radical & Community Bookshop. Special thanks to Rowan Wilson from Verso Books. Thanks also to Grosvenor, Edmund Kirby and Paul Houghton from Downing.

Danica Dakić would like to thank Stephen Attwater, Dagmar Deuring, Lorenzo Fusi, Jean Harper, Carol Hickey, Neil Jackson, Gabriele Koeppe, Julia Koeppen, Erika Kiffl, Mike Langstaff, Annie MacLean, Frances Loeffler, Barry Mardell, Kathy Mardell, Frank Richardson, Rajwant Sandhu, Alan Smith, and all those who have helped make this project possible. With special thanks to St George's Hall.

Raymond Pettibon
Thanks to Wendy Dixon from Frensons.

Will Kwan would like to thank Michelle Hodgson at Flags Unlimited, Barbara Fischer, Lorenzo Fusi, and The Canada Council for the Arts. Thanks also to Paul Houghton from Downing.

Freee
Thanks to Grosvenor and Edmund Kirby.

Karmelo Bermejo would like to thank Maisterravalbuena Gallery. Thanks also to Grosvenor and Edmund Kirby.

Cristina Lucas
Thanks to Juana de Aizpuru, Fernado Sánchez Castillo, Paul Houghton, Lorenzo Fusi, David Farnworth, Marta Rincón, Amanprit Sandhu, Leon Seth, Raj Sandhu and Martin Wallace. Thanks also to Paul Houghton from Downing.

Tala Madani would like to thank I would like to thank Lombard-Freid Gallery, Pilar Corrias Gallery and Cristian Alexa. Thanks also to Wendy Dixon from Frensons.

Kris Martin would like to thank everybody involved, with special thanks to Julia Köhler and Diana Hunnewinkel at Galerie Sies & Höke; Bill Harpe and Steven Knocker at the Black-e, Liverpool and the team at Bisk Italia.

NS Harsha
Thanks to Erin Manns and the team at Victoria Miro Gallery, Vijay Kumar C S, Mahesh B L, Srikant G for their assistance and MAS Furnitures, Mysore, for fabrication support. Thanks also to Grosvenor and Edmund Kirby.

Do Ho Suh would like to give special thanks to all involved in the project. Thanks also to Homes and Communities Agency and Wendy Dixon from Frensons.

Ryan Trecartin would like to thank the Fabric Workshop and Museum, Philadelphia; the Goetz Collection, Munich; The Moore Space – Craig Robins, Rosa de la Cruz and Silvia Cubiña, Miami; Bill and Charlotte Ford; Lauren Cornell; Elizabeth Dee; Jayne Drost; Lizzie Fitch; Jessica Gatson; Rhett LaRue; Kevin McGarry; Ashland Mines; Jenny Moore; Linda Norden; Sergio Pastor; PEW; Tim Saltarelli; Cathy, Dell and Adam Trecartin; Jack Wolgin.

Minerva Cuevas
With special thanks to Harry Swan. Thanks also to Grosvenor and Edmund Kirby.

Meschac Gaba
Thanks to Alexandra Gaba-van Dongen, Florent Tomède, Ibrahim and the whole Cotonou team, as well as Lorenzo Fusi, Liverpool Biennial and its team for supporting the realisation of the Souvenir Palace. With special thanks to Donna Berry and all the volunteers that worked so hard on this project and Liverpool Personal Preservation Society (PSS). Thanks also to Grosvenor and Edmund Kirby.

Lee Mingwei would like to thank: Rudy Tseng, Frances Loeffler, Lorenzoi Fusi, Lewis Biggs, John Rivett and everyone at Lombard Freid Projects for all their support. With special thanks to Rosalind Hyde. Thanks also to Grosvenor and Edmund Kirby.

Julieta Aranda and Anton Vidokle
Thanks to Grosvenor and Edmund Kirby.

Daniel Knorr
Thanks to Grosvenor and Edmund Kirby.

Oren Eliav would like to thank Lorenzo Fusi for coming all the way to my Tel Aviv studio and the team at Braverman Gallery Tel Aviv: Yaffa Braverman, Adi Gura and Yael Caron. Thanks also to Grosvenor and Edmund Kirby.

Tim Eitel
Thanks to Grosvenor and Edmund Kirby.

Edi Hila
Thanks to Grosvenor and Edmund Kirby.

Csaba Kis Róka would like to thank Ada,
my family, acb Gallery, Gábor Pados, all
of my friends, venice painters, baroque
masters, good wines.... Thanks also to
Grosvenor and Edmund Kirby.

Aime Mpane
Thanks to Grosvenor and Edmund Kirby.

Y. Z. Kami
Thanks to Grosvenor and Edmund Kirby.

Markus Schinwald
Thanks to Grosvenor and Edmund Kirby.

Zbyněk Sedlecký
Thanks to Grosvenor and Edmund Kirby.

Ranjani Shetter
Thanks to Talwar Gallery, New York & New
Delhi.

Nicholas Hlobo
Thanks to Michael Stevenson Gallery,
Cape Town.

Daniel Bozhkof
Thanks to Andrew Kreps Gallery, New
York.

Carol Rama
Thanks to Alexandra Wetzel and Franco
Masoero, and the gracious assistance of
lenders and private collections.

Yves Netzhammer would like to thank
Zuzana Ponicanova, Seraina Borner,
Daniel Rieben and Bernd Schure.

Franz West would like to thank Vahktang
Sirbiladze for inspiration.

Nina Canell would like to thank Aida
Strkljevic, Robin Watkins and Norman
Veitch & Grainne Sweeney at the National
Glass Centre in Sunderland for their kind
assistance and professional advice.

Tehching Hsieh
I would like to thank my mother
Su-Chiung Hung; my friend Cheng Wei
Kuong; Sean, Cecile, Maureen and the
team at Sean Kelly Gallery; as well as
Lewis, Mike, Heather and the team
from FACT.

YOUR GUIDE TO THE VERY BEST OF CULTURE AND COUNTRYSIDE IN ENGLAND'S NORTHWEST

To get your copy go to
www.primenorthwest.co.uk

Liverpool Biennial staff

Liverpool Biennial

Lewis Biggs	Director
Lisa Bradshaw	Development Officer
Paul Domela	Programme Director: Higher Education and International Exchange
Zainab Djavanroodi	International Intern
Steven Dobbins	Production and Installation Coordinator
Lorenzo Fusi	International Curator
Franny George	Partnership Coordinator
Samantha Jones	Phd Scholar
Paul Kelly	HMR Project Manager
Mary Linnell-Simmons	Marketing and Communications Officer
Frances Loeffler	Curatorial Assistant: Public Realm
Sally Lupton	Development Manager
Peter Merrington	Visitor Services Manager
Depa Miah	Visitor Services Facilitator
Allison Mottram	Finance Assistant
Laurie Peake	Programme Director: Public Art
Antony Pickthall	Head of Marketing and Communications
Carol Ramsay	Public Art Assistant
Amanprit Sandhu	Curatorial Assistant
Raj Sandhu	Projects Curator
Leon Seth	Curatorial Assistant: Host Venues
Toby Startup	Operations Coordinator
Paul Smith	Executive Director
Melanie Thorpe	Executive Officer
Daniella Trentin	Marketing Intern
Sacha Waldron	Programme Assistant: HE &IE
Richard Wilson	Finance Officer

the Bluecoat

Phil Bridges	Communications Officer
Barry Charlton	Gallery Technician
Denise Courcoux	Gallery Coordinator
Helen Dunnett	Director of Marketing & Communications
Rachel Goodsall	Marketing & Communications Assistant
Sara-Jayne Parsons	Exhibitions Curator
Laura Pilgrim	Participation Coordinator
Phil Olsen	Marketing & Audience Development Officer

Tate Liverpool

Barry Bentley	Deputy Art Handling Manager
Cathriona Bourke	Youth and Community Curator
Abigail Christenson	Schools Outreach Curator
Peter Gorschlueter	Curator
Dr. Christoph Grunenberg	Director, Tate Liverpool
Ami Guest	Press Assistant
Davinia Gregory	Curatorial Intern
Jonathan Hering	Young Music Producer
Ros Hyde	
Ian Malone	Design and Print Officer
Jennifer Martin	Marketing Officer
Alex O'Neill	(formerly) Press Assistant
Caitlin Page	Public Programmes Curator
Jemima Pyne	Head of Communications
Ken Simons	Art Handling Manager
Rachel Skelton	Press Officer
Aida Strkljevic	Assistant Curator
Carly Townsend	Marketing Assistant
Delphine Verron	Learning and Education Intern

Open Eye Gallery

Partick Henry	Director
Naomi Horlock	Creative Collaborators Project Manager
Stephanie O'Loughlin	Gallery Co-ordinator

A Foundation

Anthony Bennett
Helen Brierley
Mike Carney
Clare Warren
Mark Waugh

Interns
Nick Strowbridge
Mar de Prada

FACT

Joan Burnett	Visitor's Services Manager
Jen Chapman	Marketing and Promotions Officer
Heather Corcoran	Curator
Lucie Davies	PR & Communications Officer
Louise Latter	Young People's Coordinator
Chris Miller	Exhibitions Manager
Ellie Overs	Projects Coordinator
Edwin Pink	Tenantspin Producer
Stuart Roberts	Online Marketing Coordinator
Mike Stubbs	Director/CEO
Julia Youngman	Projects Coordinator

Liverpool Biennial would like to thank everyone who supports us and works with us

Principal Funders

Liverpool Biennial was founded by James Moores with the support of
A Foundation

Gulbenkian European Commissions

CALOUSTE
GULBENKIAN
FOUNDATION

The Calouste Gulbenkian Foundation is supporting a series of new commissions by European artists over a three-year period from 2008–2010. Within *Touched*, the artists commissioned as part of this award include Rosa Barba, Emese Benczúr, Daniel Bozhkov, Nina Canell, Danica Dakić, Wannes Goetschalckx, Eva Kot'átková, Lars Laumann, Antti Laitinen, Cristina Lucas, Kris Martin, Yves Netzhammer and Franz West.

Official Hotel Partner

National Media Partner

Visitor Services Partner

Project Sponsors

Supporters

Festival Partners

A Foundation

the Bluecoat.

FACT
FOUNDATION FOR ART AND
CREATIVE TECHNOLOGY

OpenEyeGallery

LIVERPOOL
TATE

Bloomberg
newcontemporaries
2010

Walker
Art Gallery

National Museums Liverpool

John Moores
Painting Prize

 COOPERATIVE

CONTEMPORARY
URBAN
CENTRE
www.contemporaryurbancentre.org

 NO LONGER EMPTY
ON THE ROAD

 S.Q.U.A.T.
LIVERPOOL 2010